westlife

COAST TO COAST

WISE PUBLICATIONS
London/New York/Sydney/Paris/Copenhagen/Madrid/Tokyo

£9.95

MY LOVE

Words & Music by Jörgen Elofsson, Pelle Nylén, David Kreuger & Per Magnusson

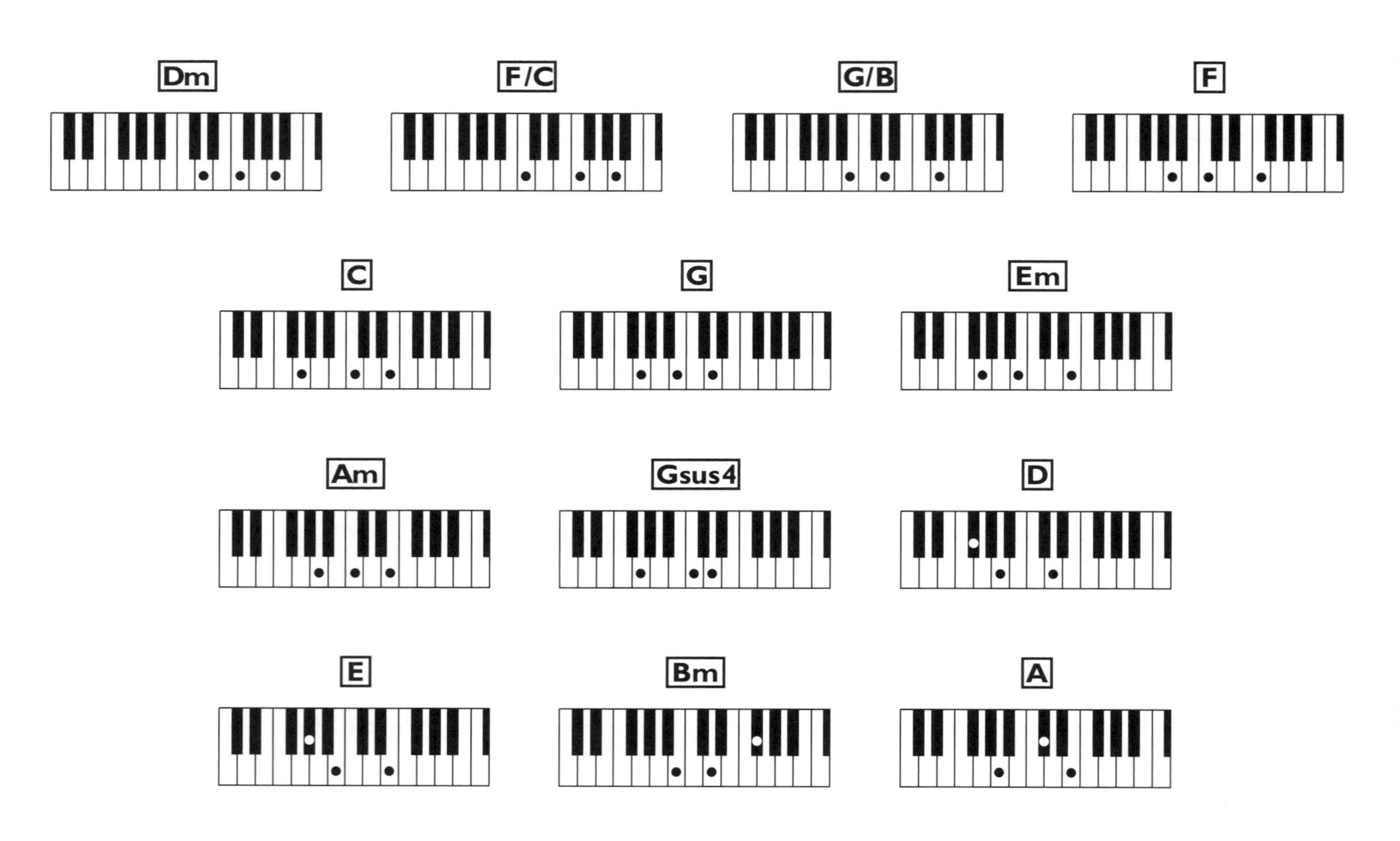

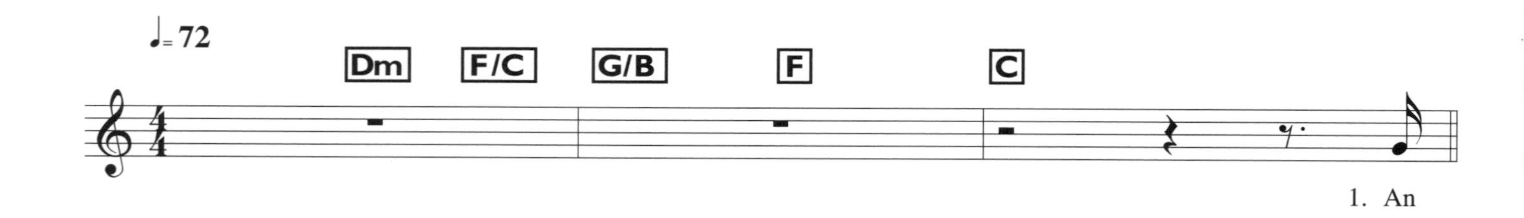

Gsus4 G C G Em Am
- er. I won - der how, I won - der why, I won - der where they are, the

F D Gsus4 G Dm F/C G/B
days we had, the songs we sang to - geth - er, oh yeah. And oh my love, I'm

C F Dm F Gsus4 G
hold - ing on for - ev - er, reach - ing for a love that seems so far. So I

F C F C
say a lit - tle prayer and hope my dreams will take me there, where the

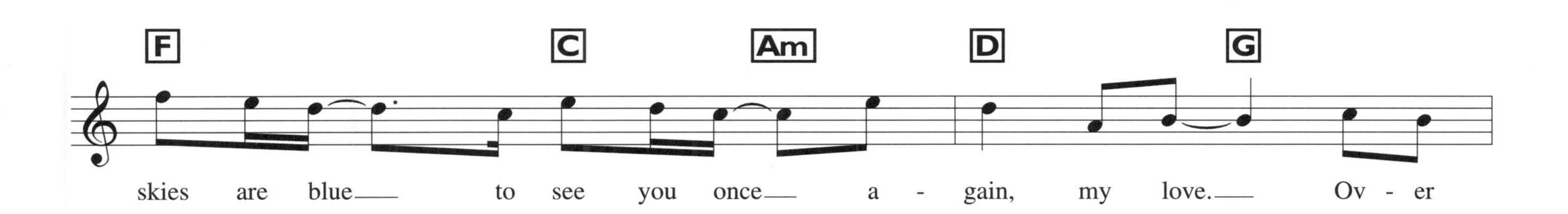
F C Am D G
skies are blue to see you once a - gain, my love. Ov - er

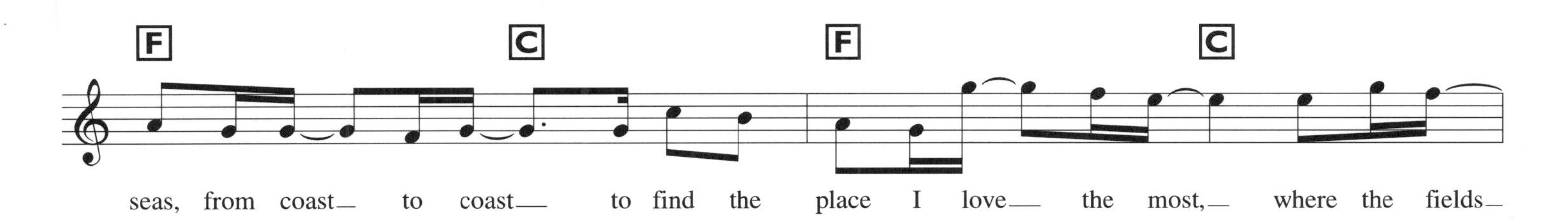
F C F C
seas, from coast to coast to find the place I love the most, where the fields

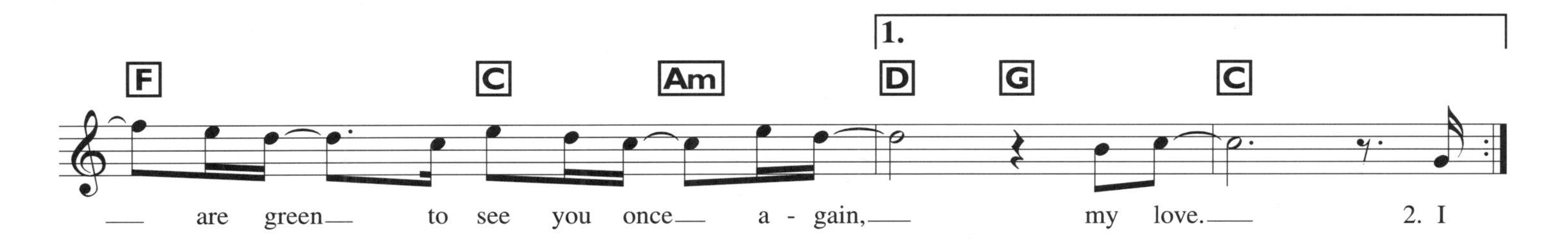
1.
F C Am D G C
are green to see you once a - gain, my love. 2. I

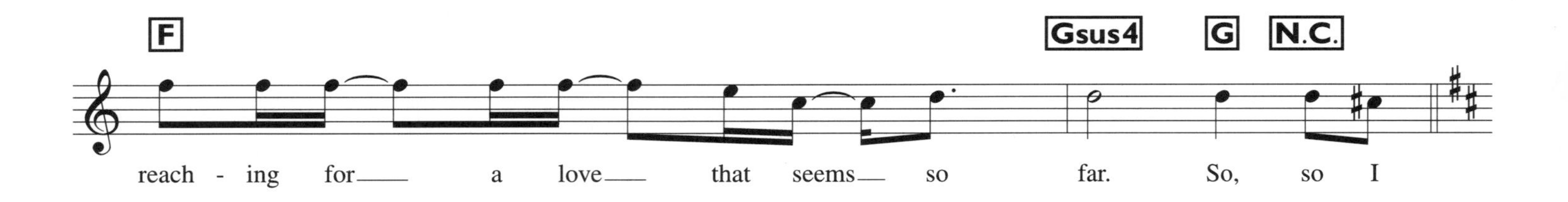

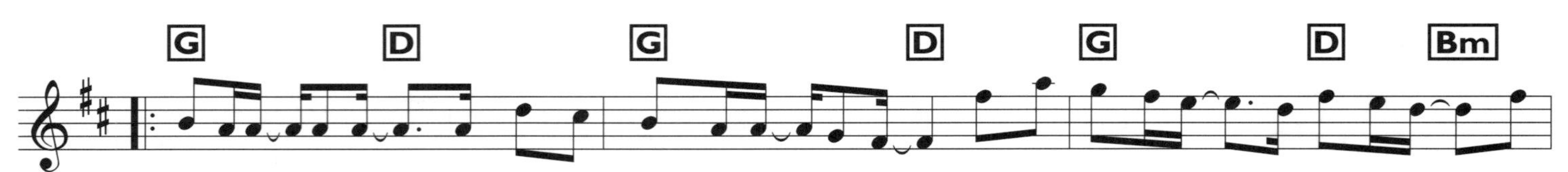

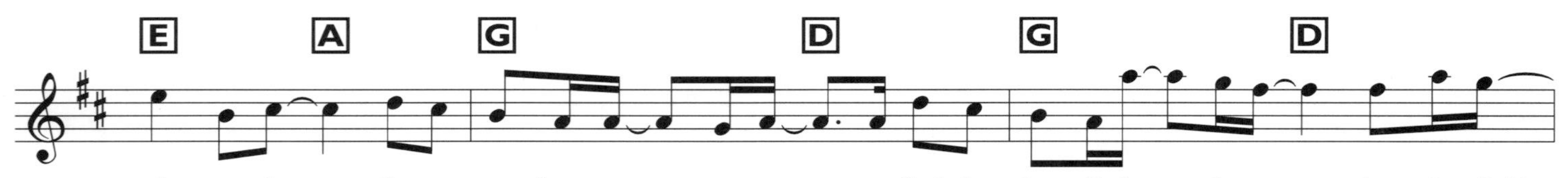

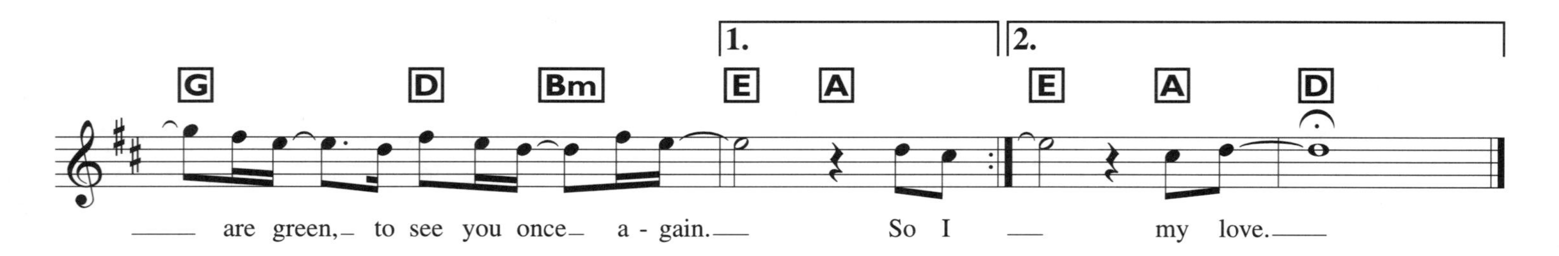

Verse 2:
I try to read, I go to work
I'm laughing with my friends
But I can't stop to keep myself from thinking, oh no.
I wonder how, I wonder why
I wonder where they are
The days we had, the songs we sang together, oh yeah.

WHAT MAKES A MAN

Words & Music by Steve Mac & Wayne Hector

E/G♯ B/D♯ F♯ E F♯
oth - er girl, I'd let you walk a - way, an - y

E/G♯ B/D♯ F♯ E E/F♯
oth-er girl, I'm sure I'd be O. K. Tell me what makes a man

B F♯ G♯m C♯m B/D♯
wan-na give you all his heart, smile when you're a - round, and cry when you're a - part?

E E/F♯ B F♯
If you know what makes a man wan-na love you the way I do,

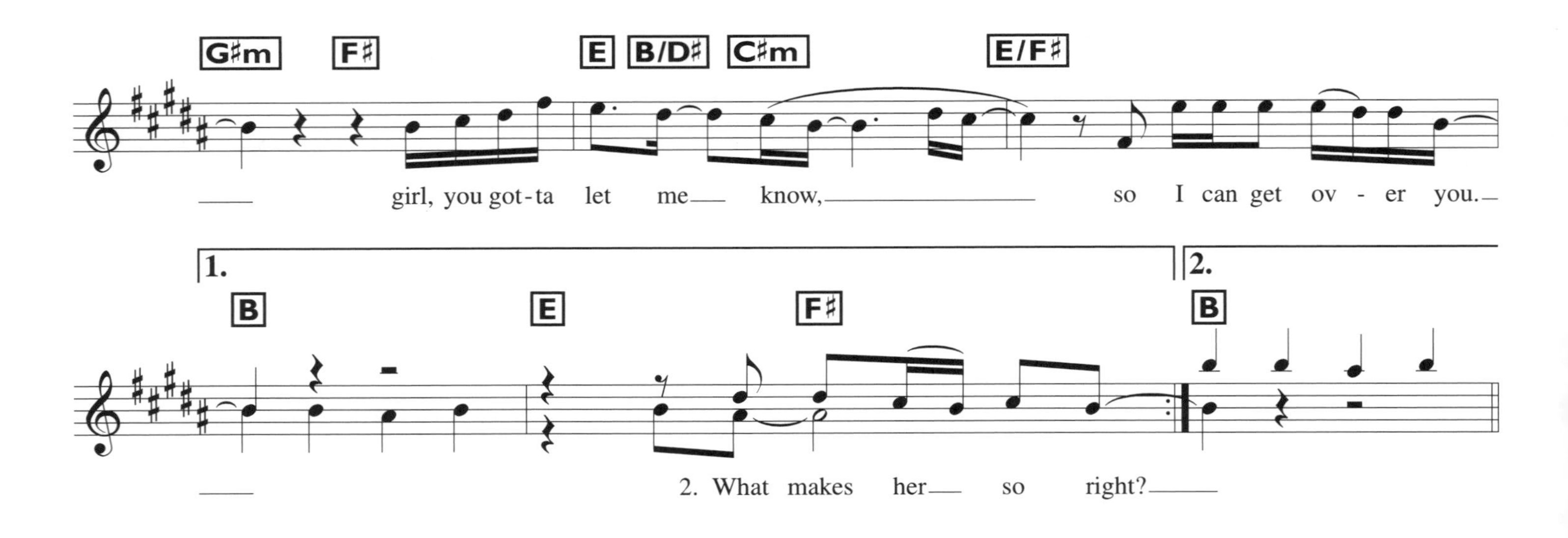
G♯m F♯ E B/D♯ C♯m E/F♯
girl, you got-ta let me know, so I can get ov - er you.
1.
2.
B E F♯ B
2. What makes her so right?

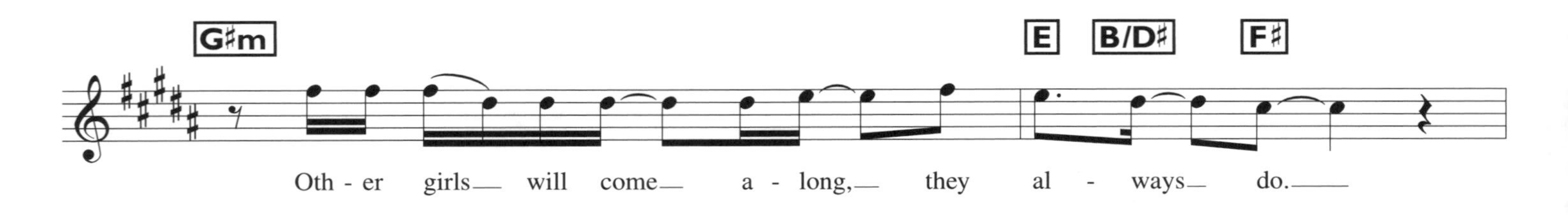
G♯m E B/D♯ F♯
Oth - er girls will come a - long, they al - ways do.

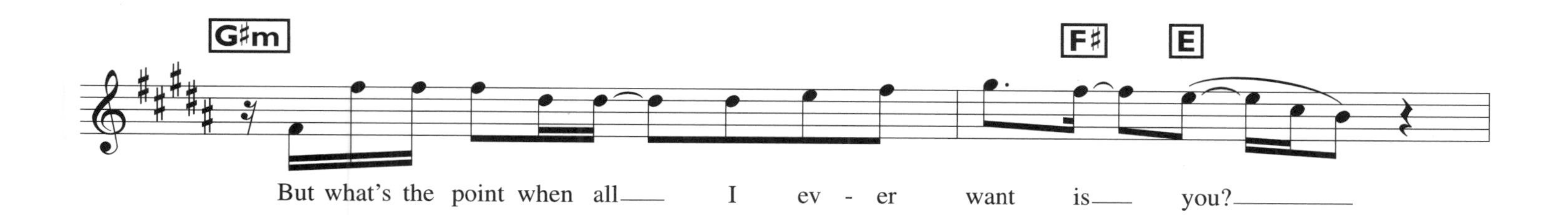

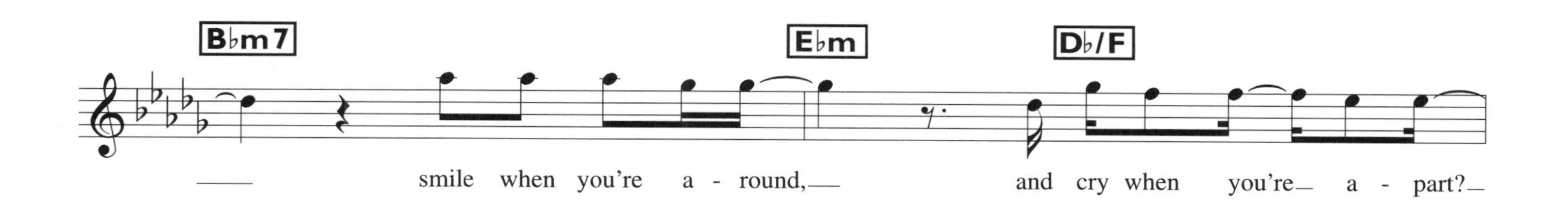

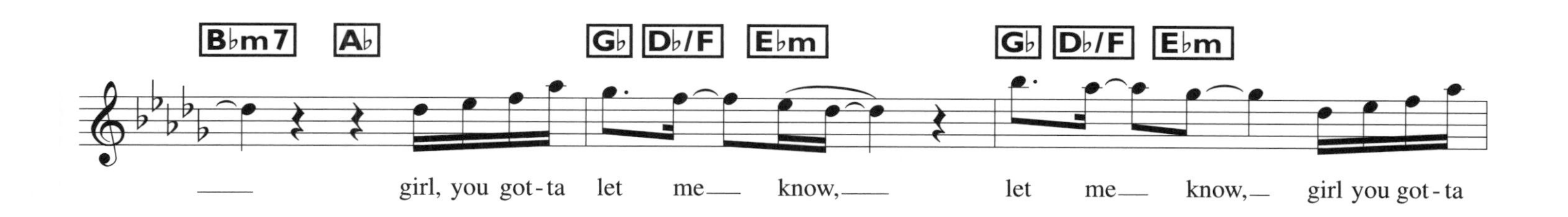

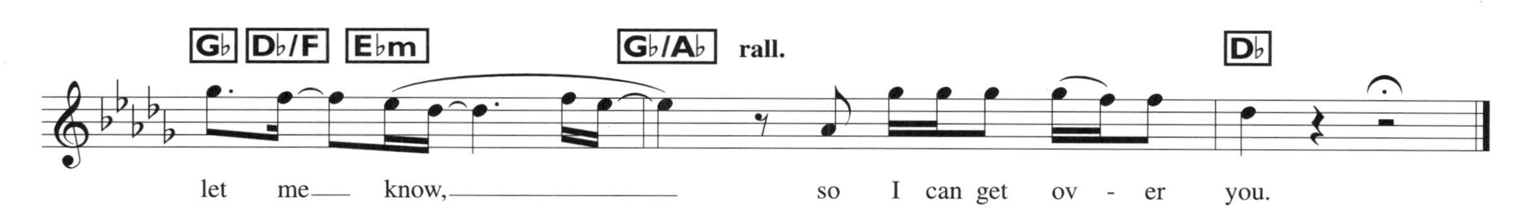

Verse 2:
What makes her so right, is it the sound of her laugh?
That look in her eyes
When do you decide she is the dream that you seek?
That force in your life.

When you apologise, no matter who was wrong
When you get on your knees, if that would bring her home.

I LAY MY LOVE ON YOU

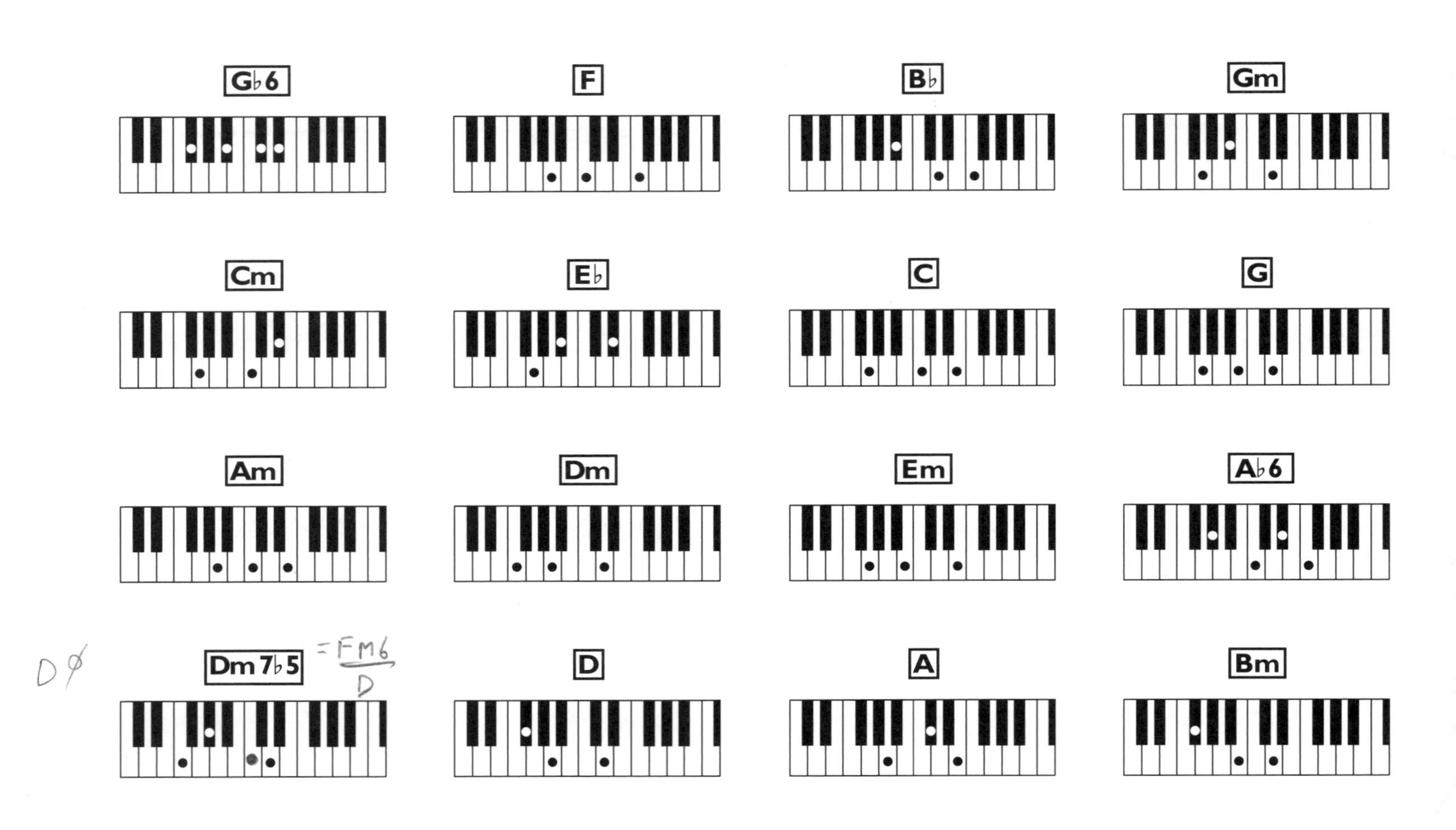

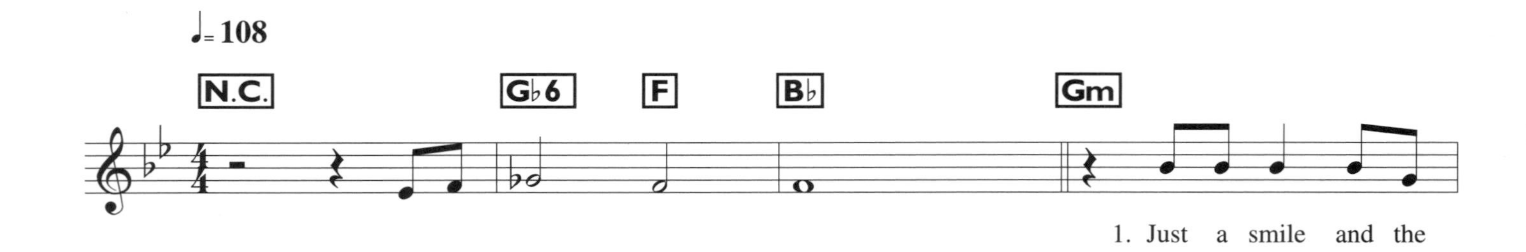

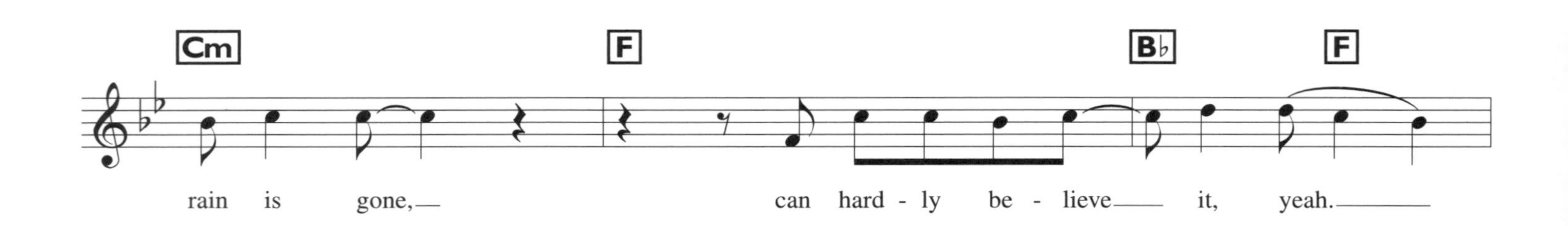

Gm Cm E♭ F B♭ F
There's an an-gel stand-ing next to me, reach-ing for my heart.
Gm Cm F B♭ F
2. Just a smile and there's no way back, can hard-ly be-lieve it, yeah.
(Verse 3 see block lyric)
Gm Cm E♭ F
But there's an an-gel call-ing me, reach-ing for my heart,
Cm B♭ E♭ F Cm B♭ F
I know that I'll be O. K. now, this time it's real. I lay my love on
C G Am F G
you, it's all I wan-na do, ev-'ry time I breathe I feel brand new. You op-en up my
C G Dm Em
heart, show me all your love and walk right through, as I
A♭6 G C Dm
1. 2.
lay my love on you.

Dm7♭5 C Dm
I never knew that love could feel so good.
Dm7♭5 Am D Dm C
Like a
F G Dm C G
once in a life - time, you change my world.
D A Bm G A
I lay my love on you, you make me feel brand new.
D A Em G A
Show me your love and walk right through, oh yeah, as I lay my love on you.
I lay my love on
D A Bm
It's all I wan - na do, ev - 'ry time I breathe, I feel brand new,
you.
G A D A
you op - en up my heart, show me all your love and walk right through,

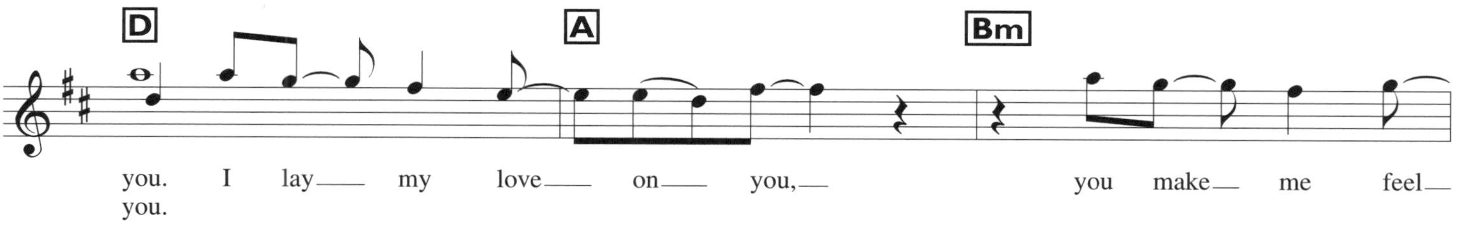

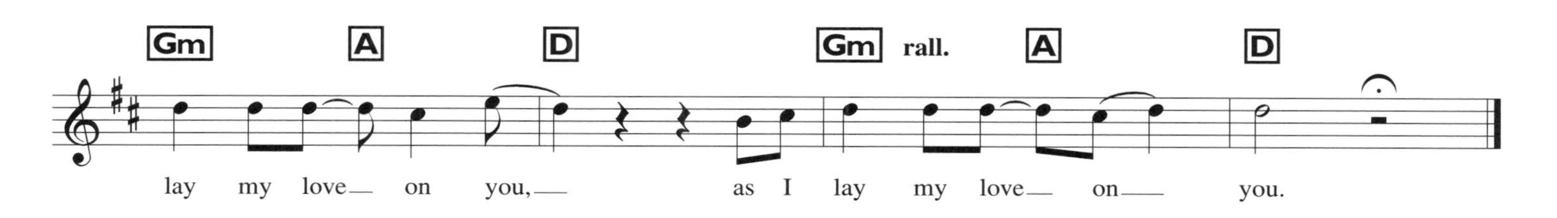

Verse 3:
I was lost in a lonely place
Could hardly believe it, yeah.
Holding on to yesterdays
Far, far too long.
Now I believe it's O.K.
Cos this time it's real.

I lay my love on you *etc.*

I HAVE A DREAM (REMIX)

Words & Music by Benny Andersson & Björn Ulvaeus

D7
G
(2º)
(3º)
the fu - ture
ev - en if
you fail.
I be - lieve in
D7
C
an - gels,
some - thing good in
ev - 'ry - thing I
G
D7
see.
I be - lieve in an - gels,
when I know the
C
G
D7
To Coda
time is right for me.
I'll cross the stream,
I have a
G
1.
dream.
2. I have a
2.
D7
G

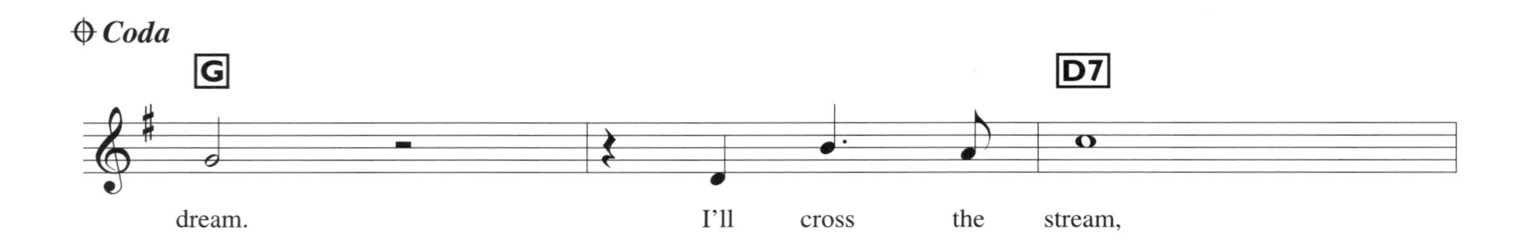

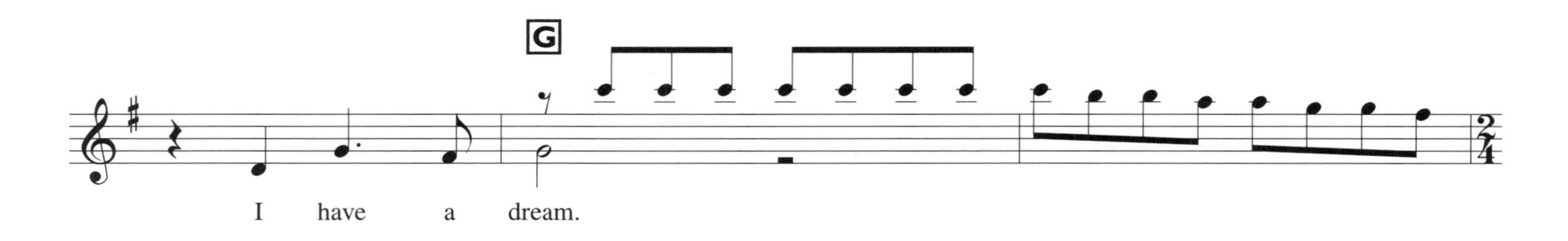

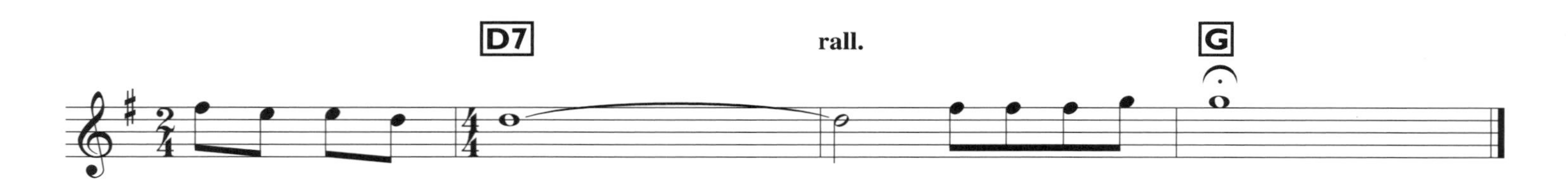

Verse 2:
I have a dream
A fantasy
To help me through
Reality.
And my destination
Makes it worth the while.
Pushing through the darkness
Still another mile.

I believe in angels *etc.*

AGAINST ALL ODDS (FEATURING MARIAH CAREY)

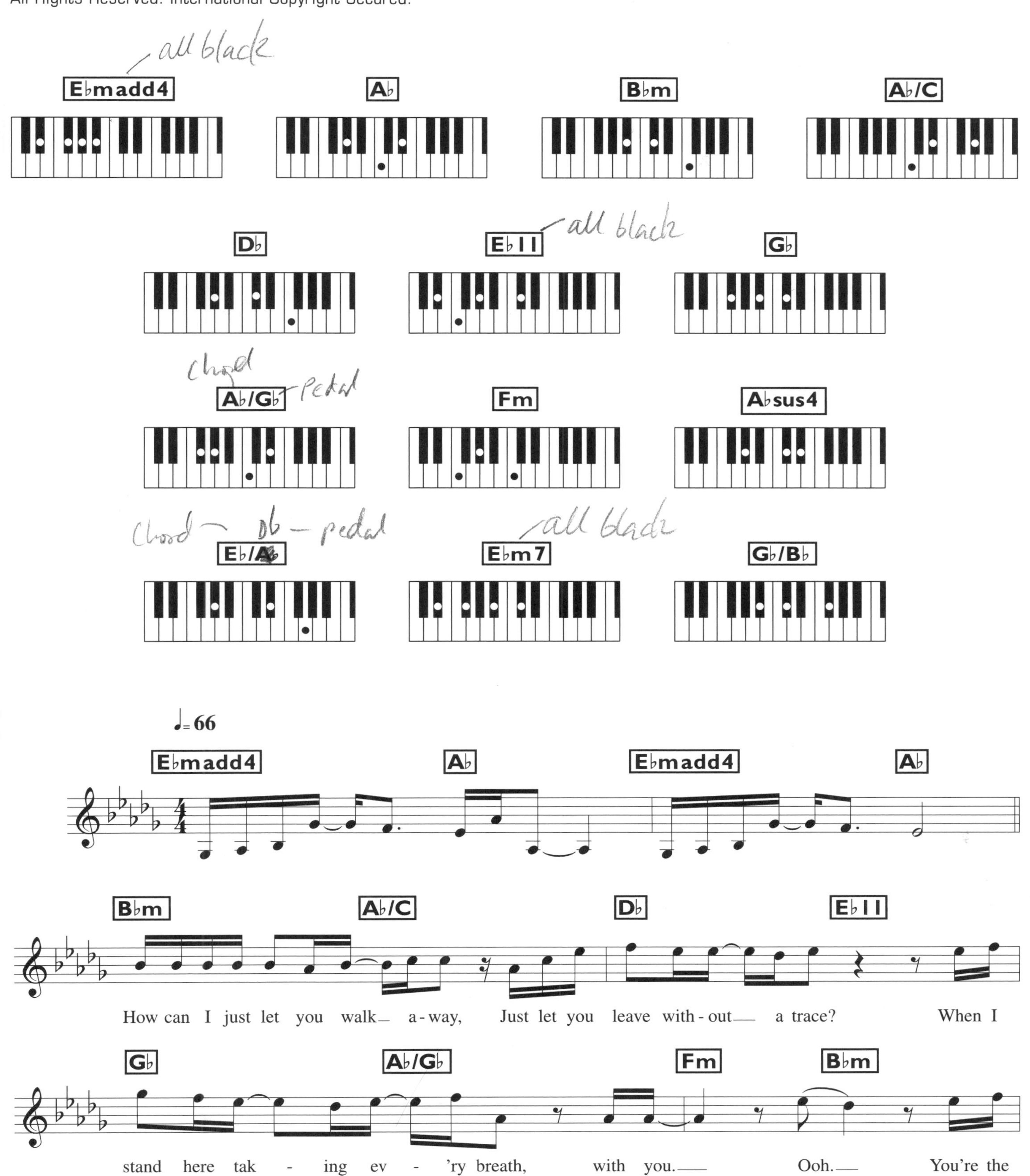

E♭madd4 G♭ A♭sus4 A♭
on - ly one who real - ly knew me at all.

B♭m A♭/C D♭ E♭11
1. How can you just walk a - way from me, when all I can do is watch you leave? Cos we've
(Verse 2 see block lyric)

G♭ A♭/G♭ Fm B♭m
shared the laugh - ter and the pain, and ev - en shared the tears. You're the

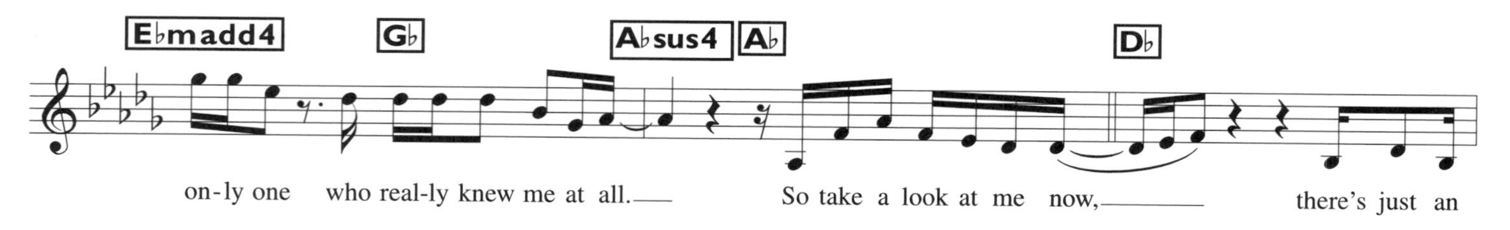
E♭madd4 G♭ A♭sus4 A♭ D♭
on-ly one who real-ly knew me at all. So take a look at me now, there's just an

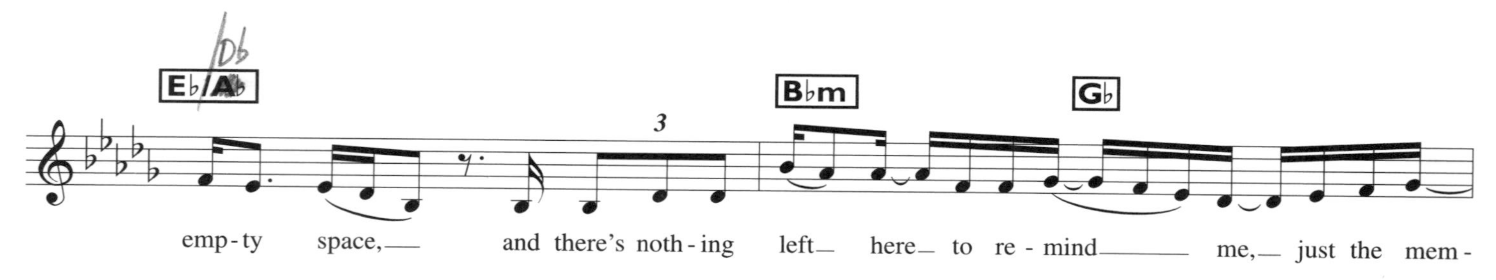
E♭/A♭ B♭m G♭
3
emp-ty space, and there's noth-ing left here to re - mind me, just the mem -

E♭m7 A♭ D♭
- 'ry of your face. So take a look at me now, there's just an

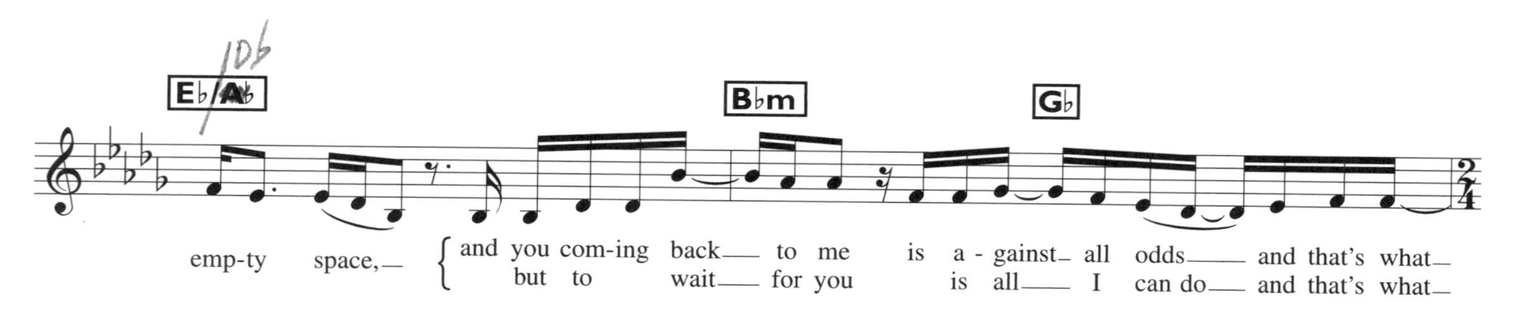
E♭/A♭ B♭m G♭
emp-ty space, and you com-ing back to me is a - gainst all odds and that's what
but to wait for you is all I can do and that's what

Verse 2:
I wish I could just make you turn around
Turn around and see me cry.
There's so much I need to say to you
So many reasons why.
You're the only one who really knew me at all.

WHEN YOU'RE LOOKING LIKE THAT

Words & Music by Rami, Andreas Carlsson & Max Martin

B F♯ E F♯
- dy who's star - ing would - n't be - lieve that this girl was mine.

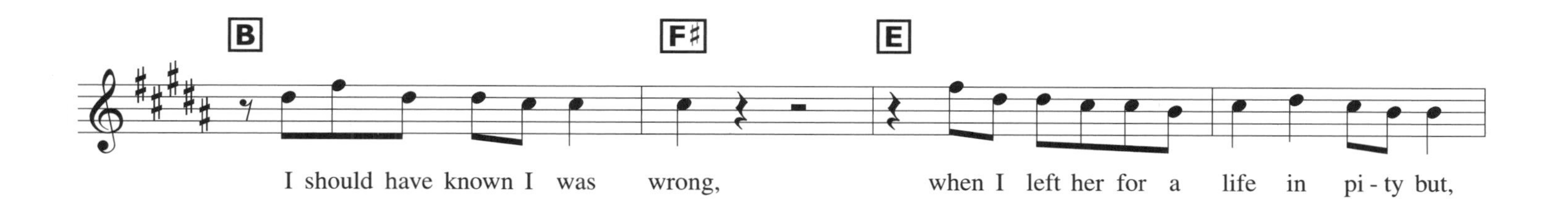
B F♯ E
I should have known I was wrong, when I left her for a life in pi - ty but,

B F♯ E F♯
they say you nev - er miss the wa - ter un - til it's gone. Guess I

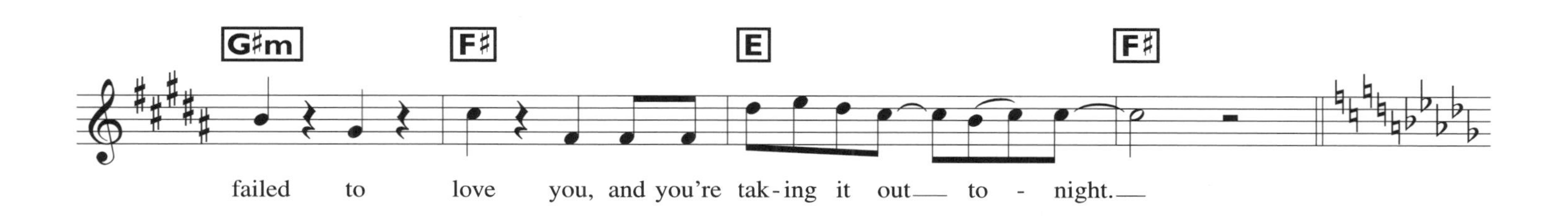
G♯m F♯ E F♯
failed to love you, and you're tak - ing it out to - night.

D♭ A♭sus4 B♭m7 G♭
How am I sup - posed to leave you now, when you're look - ing like that?

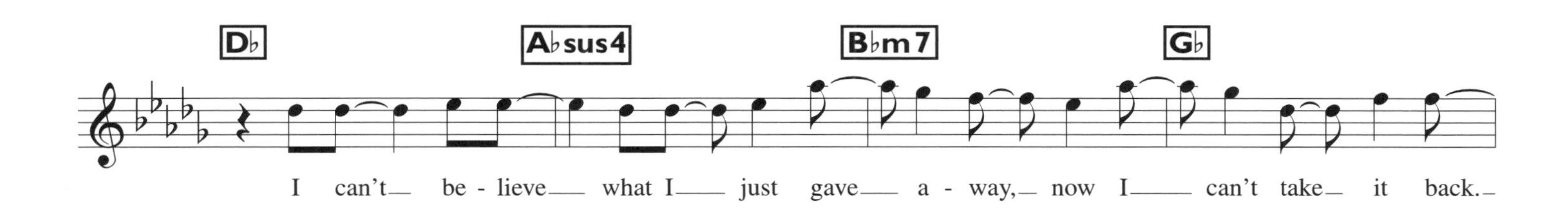
D♭ A♭sus4 B♭m7 G♭
I can't be - lieve what I just gave a - way, now I can't take it back.

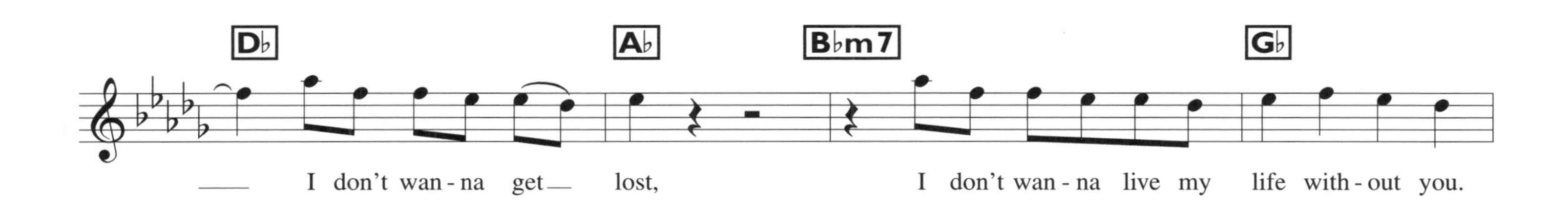
D♭ A♭ B♭m7 G♭
I don't wan - na get lost, I don't wan - na live my life with - out you.

To Coda
D♭
A♭sus4
B♭m7
G♭
How am I supposed to leave you now, when you're look-ing like

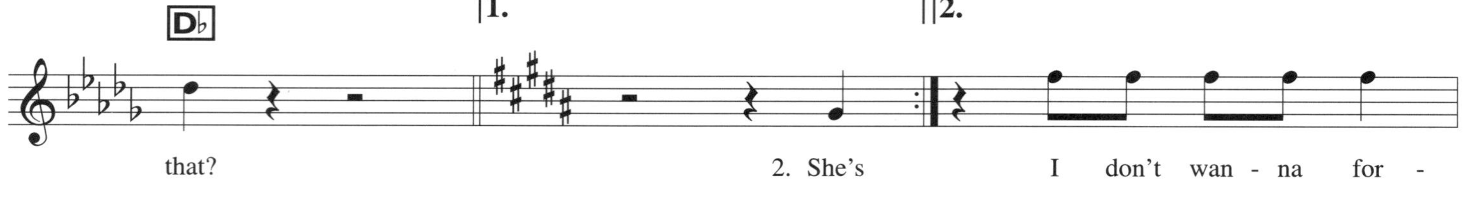
D♭
1.
2.
that? 2. She's
I don't wan-na for-

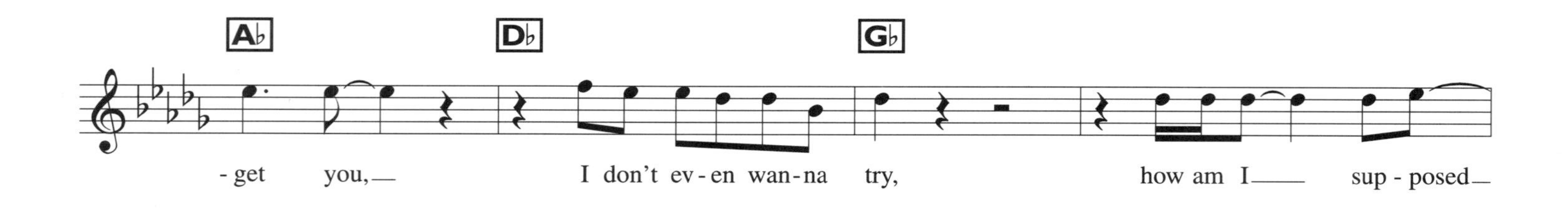
A♭
D♭
G♭
-get you, I don't ev-en wan-na try, how am I sup-posed

A♭
G♭
A♭sus4
D♭
N.C.
to walk on by, when you're look-ing like that?

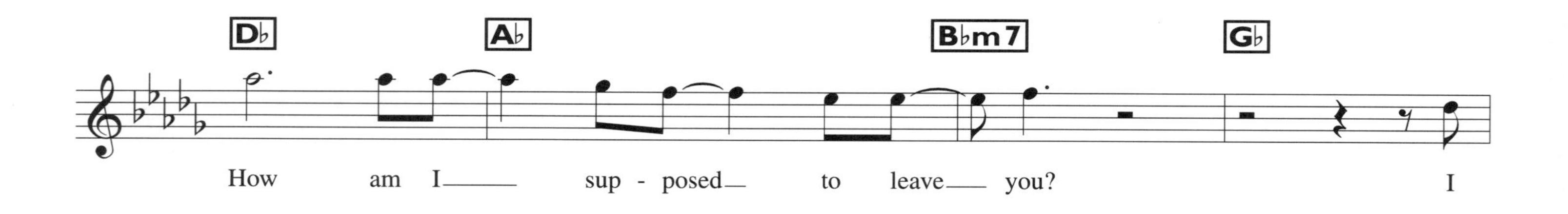
D♭
A♭
B♭m7
G♭
How am I sup-posed to leave you? I

D♭
A♭
B♭m7
G♭
can't be-lieve what I just gave a-way. Cos I can't take it
back, I'm lost, I don't wan-na live my life with-out you.
(Live my life with-out

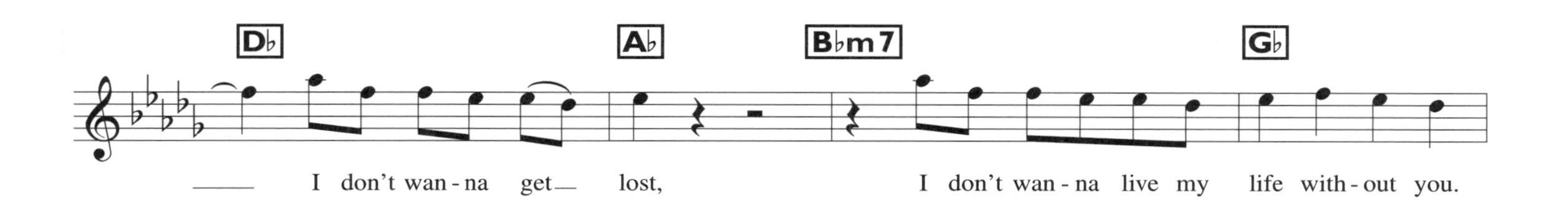

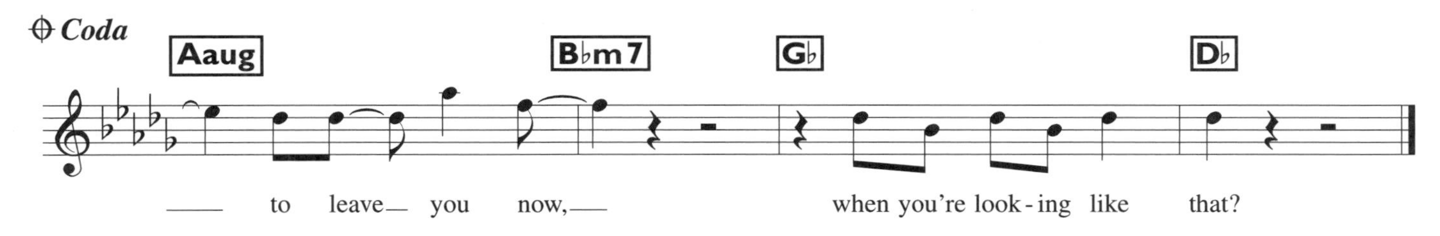

Verse 2:
She's all dressed up for glamour and rock and roll
Wanna squeeze her real tight, get out of this place if only I could take control.
But she's out of my reach forever
And just a week ago she lied next to me
It's so ironic how I had to lose just to see that I failed to love you
And you're taking it out tonight.

CLOSE

Words & Music by Steve Mac, Wayne Hector & Chris Farren

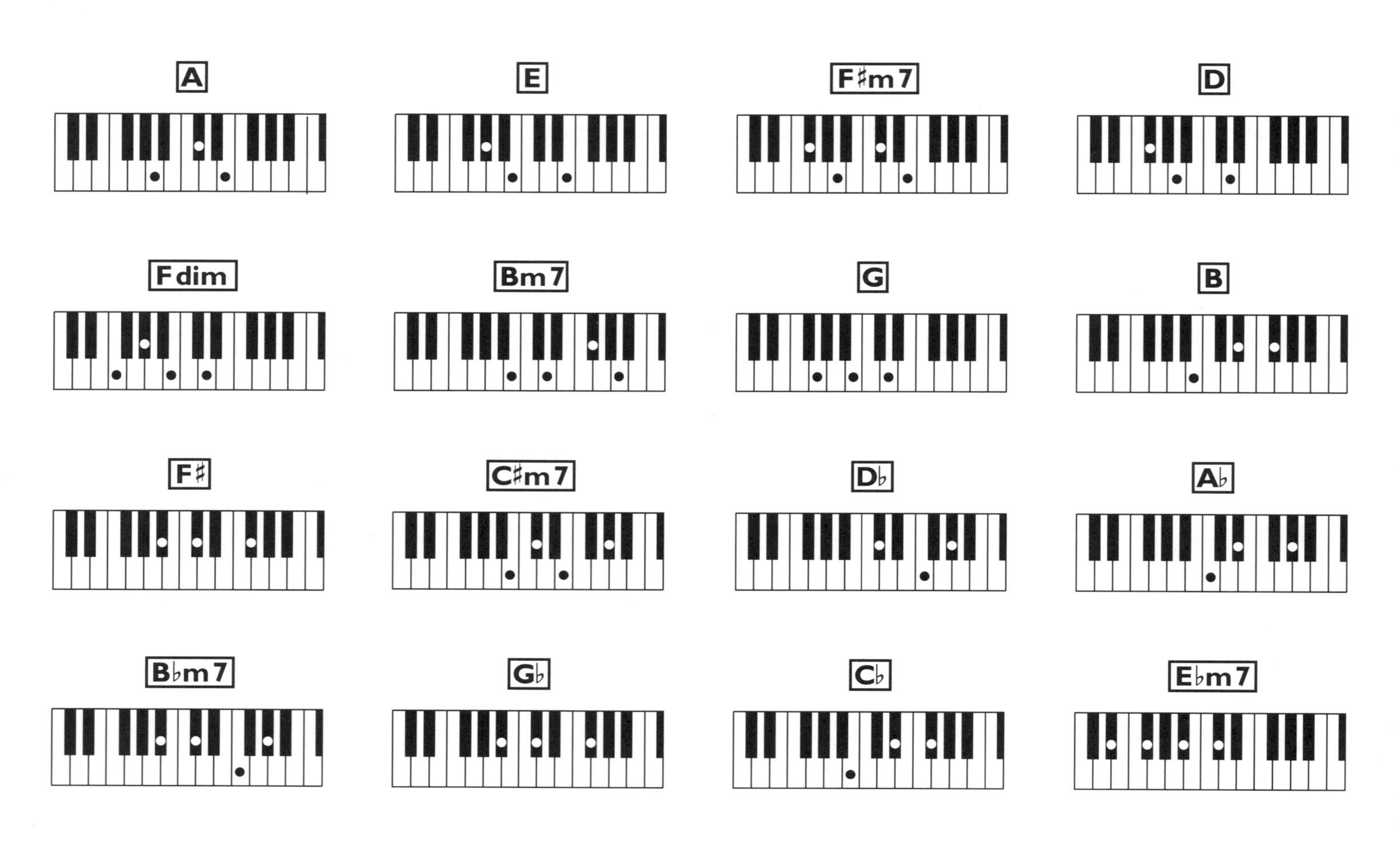

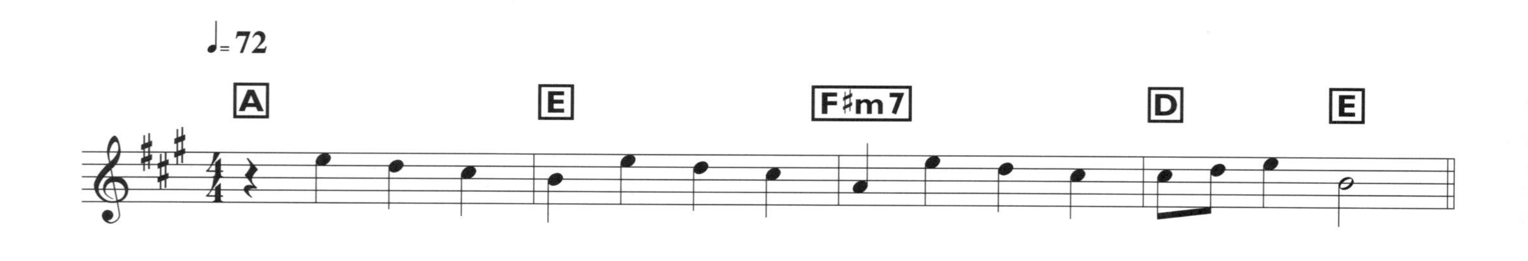

D
A
near you seem to be.
I could talk all night just to
E
Fdim
A
F♯m7
E
hear you breathe,
I could spend my life just
D
A
Bm7
E
liv - ing this dream.
1 2
You're all I'll ev - er need.
A
E
F♯m7
D
E
You give me strength, you give me hope, you give me some - one to love, some - one to hold.
A
E
G
Bm7
A
When I'm in your arms, I need you to know,
I've nev - er been, nev - er
1.
2.
D
A
D
E
G
been this close.
close.
Close e - nough to see it's true,
A
D
E
close e - nough to trust in you, clos - er now than an - y words can say, yeah.

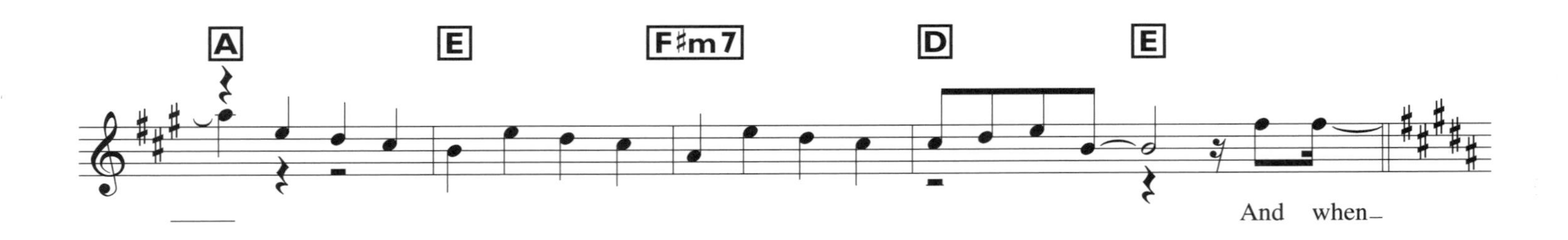

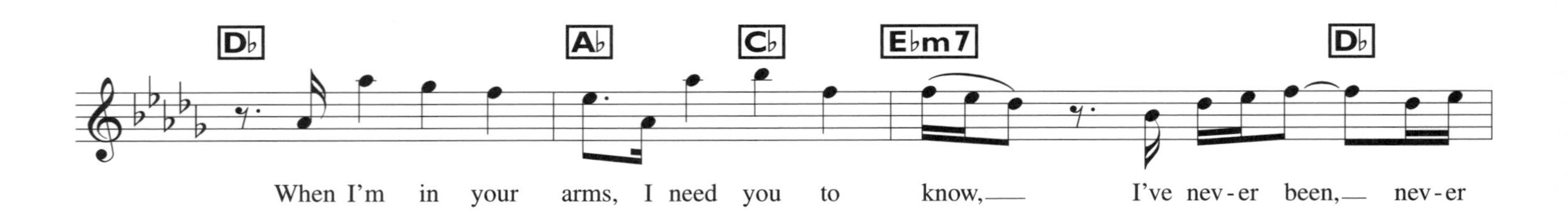

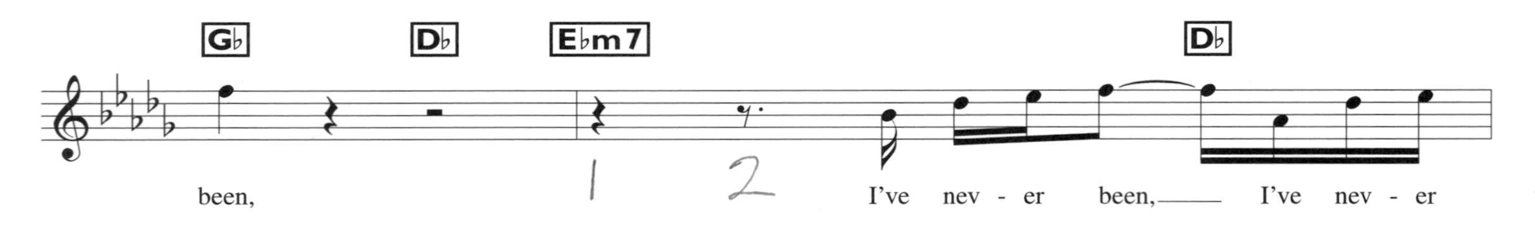

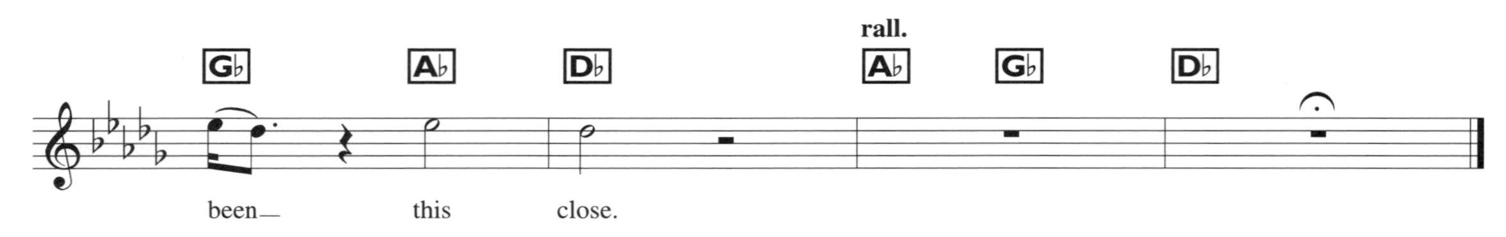

Verse 2:
With all the loves I used to know
I kept my distance, I never let go.
But in your arms I know I'm safe
Cos I've never been held and I've never been kissed in this way.
You're all I'll ever need, you're all I'll ever need.

SOMEBODY NEEDS YOU

Words & Music by Jörgen Elofsson, Andreas Carlsson & Jake

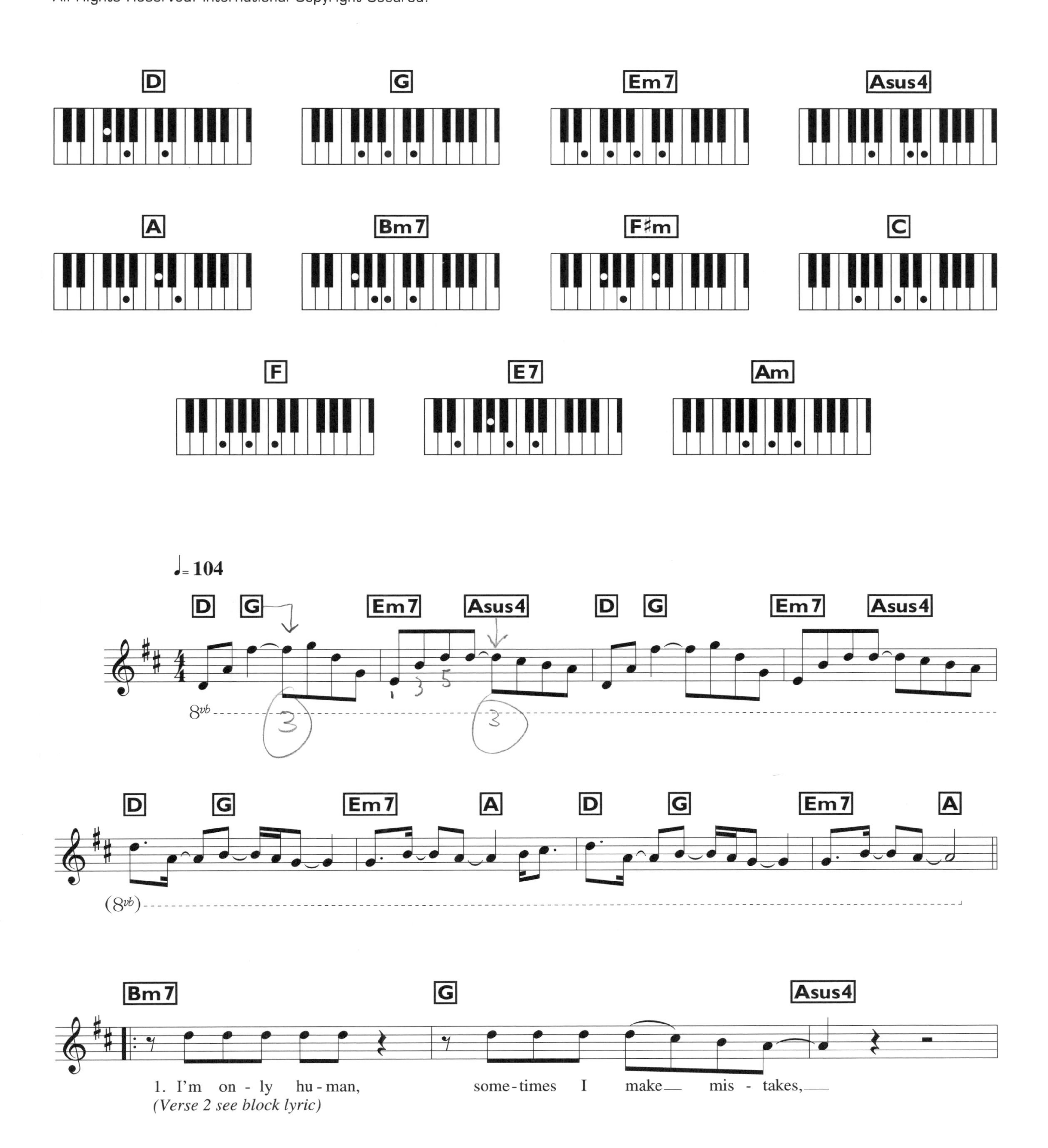

A Bm7 G
if you for - give me I'm gon - na do what it takes,

Asus4 A G A
yeah. But now I know bet - ter, to

F♯m Bm7 C Asus4 A
hurt you was wrong, girl it's with you I be - long, ooh. Some-bo-dy

D G Em7 A D G
needs you like nev - er be - fore. Some-bo-dy wants your love, ba - by

A Bm7 G A D
op - en the door. Don't you leave me a - lone, don't you turn out the light, some-bo-dy

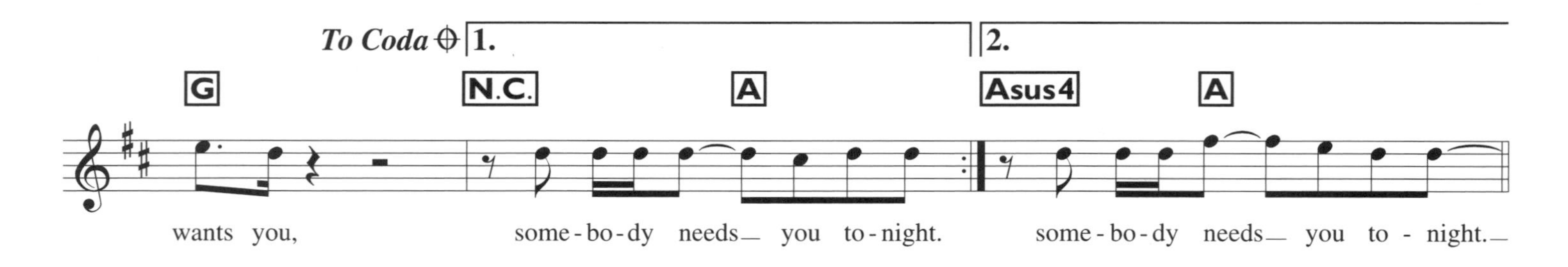
To Coda 1. 2.
G N.C. A Asus4 A
wants you, some-bo-dy needs you to-night. some-bo-dy needs you to - night.

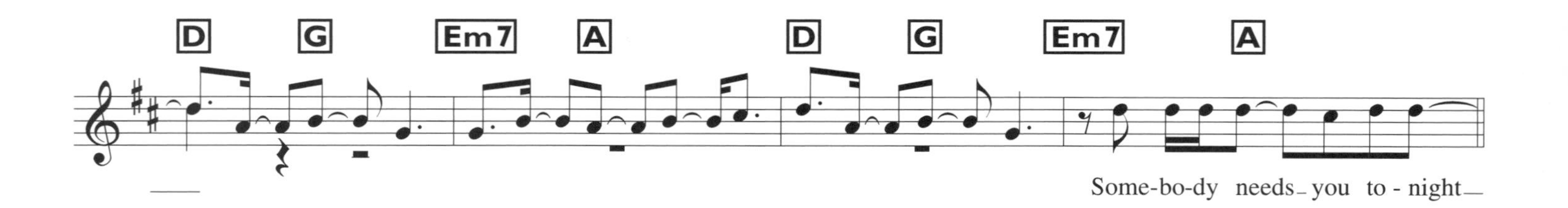
D G Em7 A D G Em7 A
Some-bo-dy needs you to - night

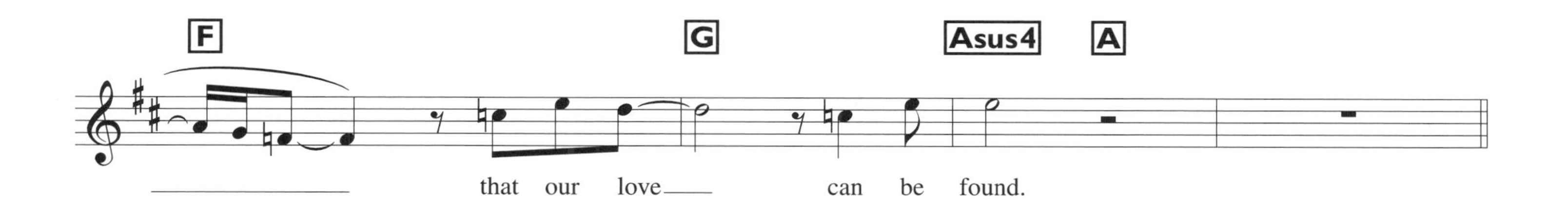

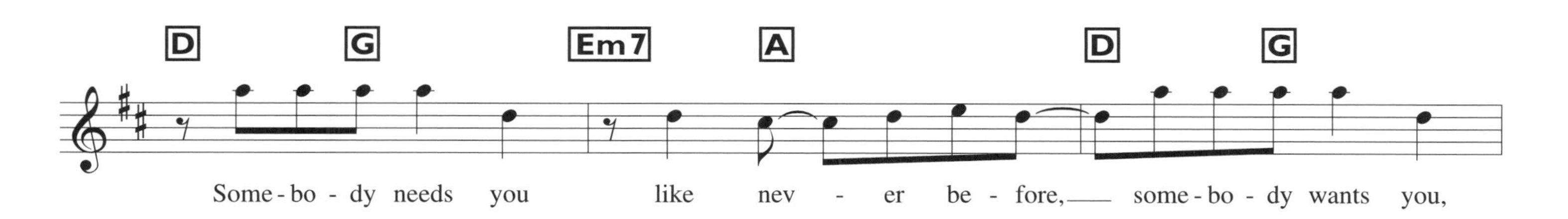

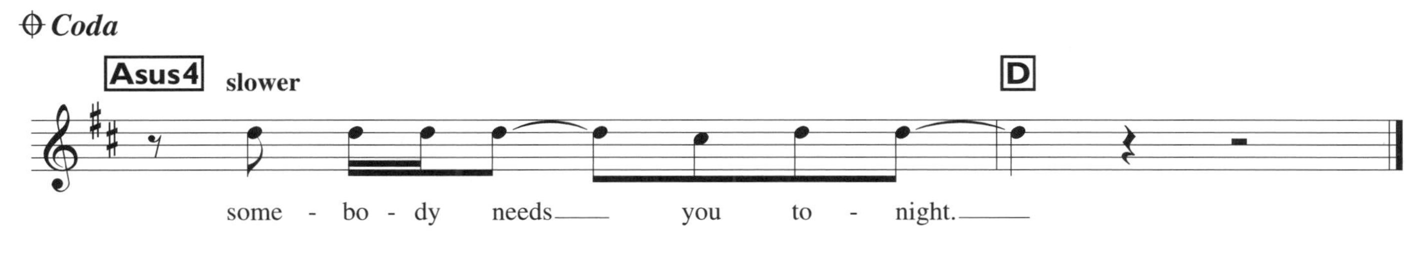

Verse 2:
I've been thinking
We should be talking it through.
You must believe me
I'll make it all up to you.
Cos now I know better
To hurt you was wrong
Girl, it's with you I belong.

ANGEL'S WINGS

Words & Music by Steve Mac, Wayne Hector & Jimmy MacCarthy

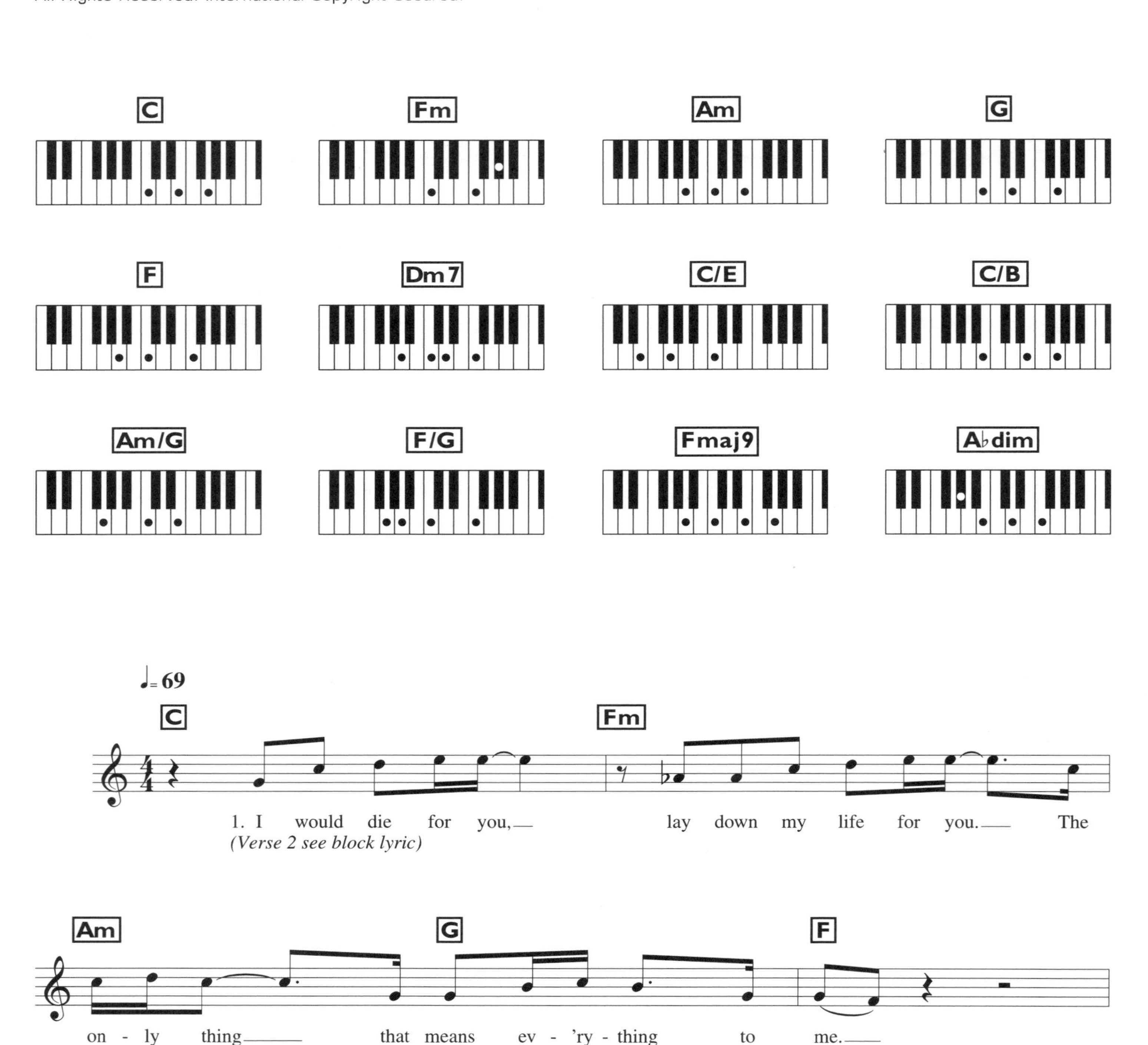

Am G F
an - y - thing I ev - er could a - chieve, and you make
Dm7 Fm
ev - 'ry - thing that used to seem so big

C/E F G
seem to be so small since you ar - rived. On an-gel's

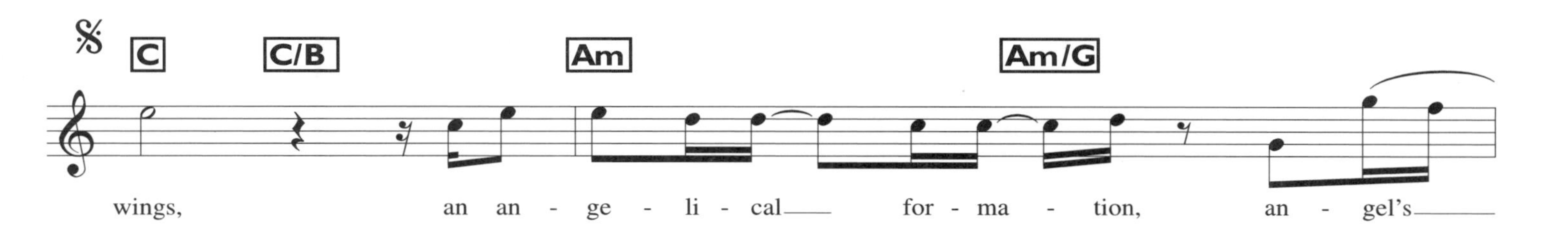

C C/B Am Am/G
wings, an an - ge - li - cal for - ma - tion, an - gel's

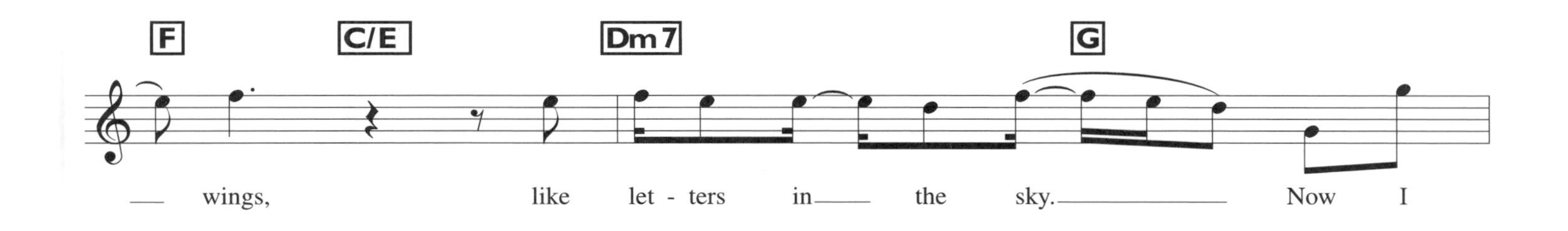

F C/E Dm7 G
wings, like let - ters in the sky. Now I

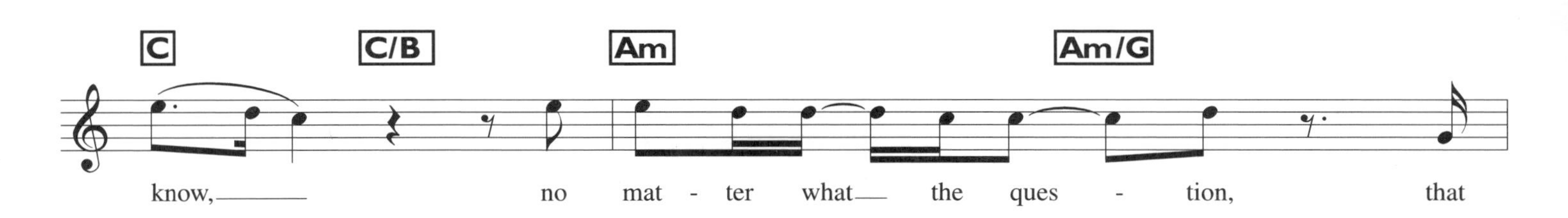

C C/B Am Am/G
know, no mat - ter what the ques - tion, that

(F)
Dm 7
6
Dm7 C/E F F/G
To Coda
love is the an - swer, it's writ - ten on an - gel's wings.

Verse 2:
And I often wonder why someone as flawed as I
Deserves to be as happy as you make me.
So as the years roll by I'll be there at your side
I'll follow you wherever your heart takes me.
Cos you make everything that used to be so big
Seem to be so small since you arrived.

SOLEDAD

Words & Music by Rami, Andreas Carlsson & K.C. Porter

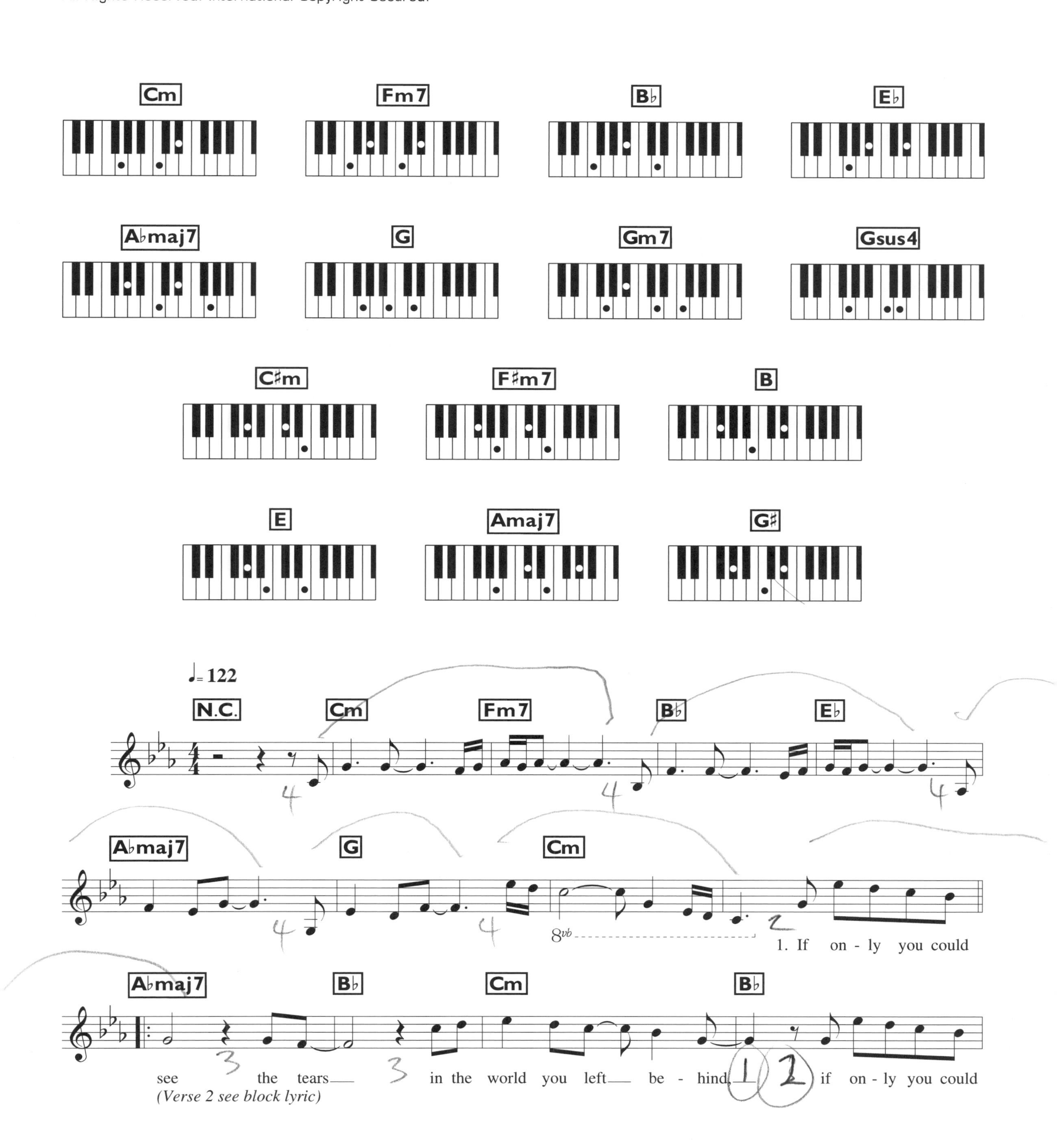

A♭maj7 B♭ Cm B♭ A♭maj7
hear my heart just one more time. Ev - en when I close my eyes,

B♭ Cm B♭ Fm7
there's an im - age of your face, and once a - gain I come to re -

Gm7 Gsus4 G
- al - ise you're a loss I can't re - place. So - le - dad,

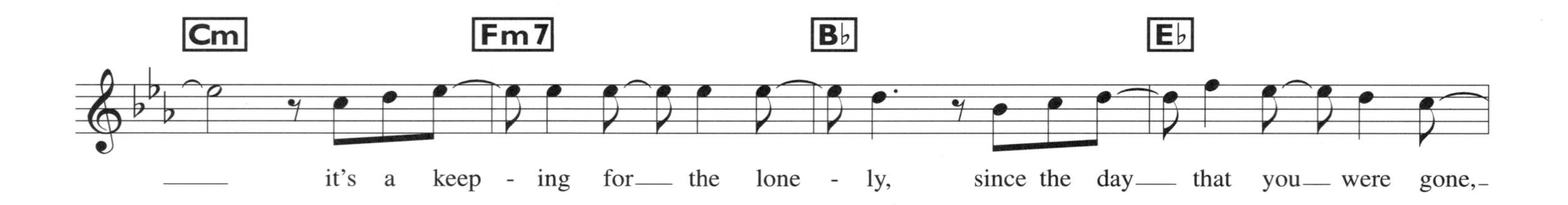
Cm Fm7 B♭ E♭
it's a keep - ing for the lone - ly, since the day that you were gone,

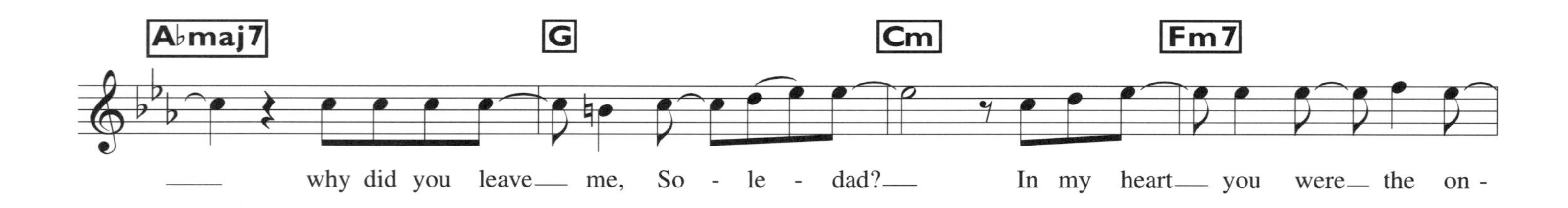
A♭maj7 G Cm Fm7
why did you leave me, So - le - dad? In my heart you were the on -

B♭ E♭ A♭maj7
- ly, and your me - mo - ry lives on, why did you leave

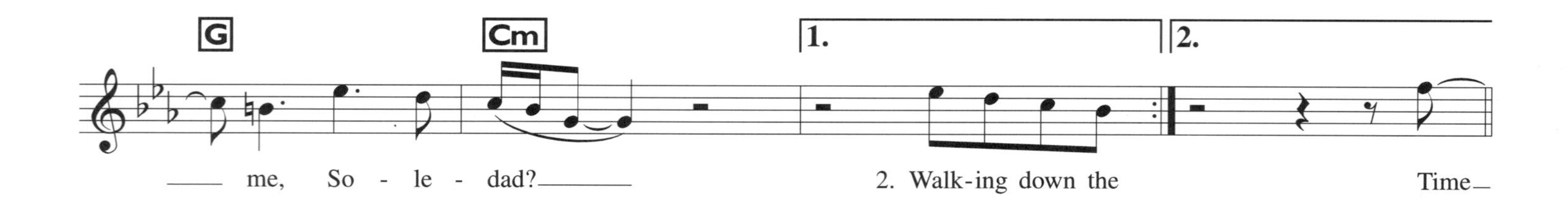
G Cm
1.
2.
me, So - le - dad? 2. Walk-ing down the Time

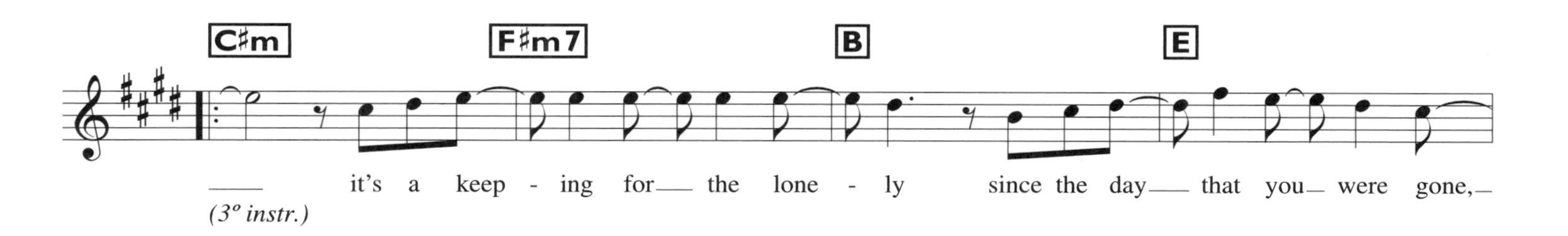

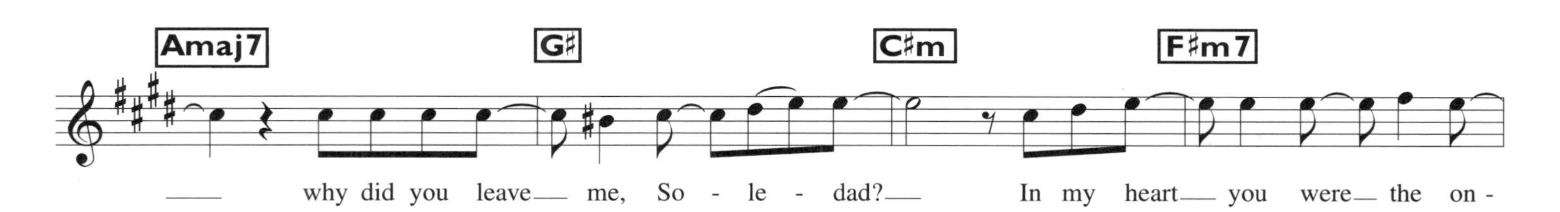

Verse 2:
Walking down the streets of Nothingville
Where our love was young and free
Can't believe just what an empty place
It has come to be.
I would give my life away
If it could only be the same
Cos I can't still the voice inside of me
That is calling out your name.

PUZZLE OF MY HEART

Words & Music by Jörgen Elofsson & Andrew Fromm

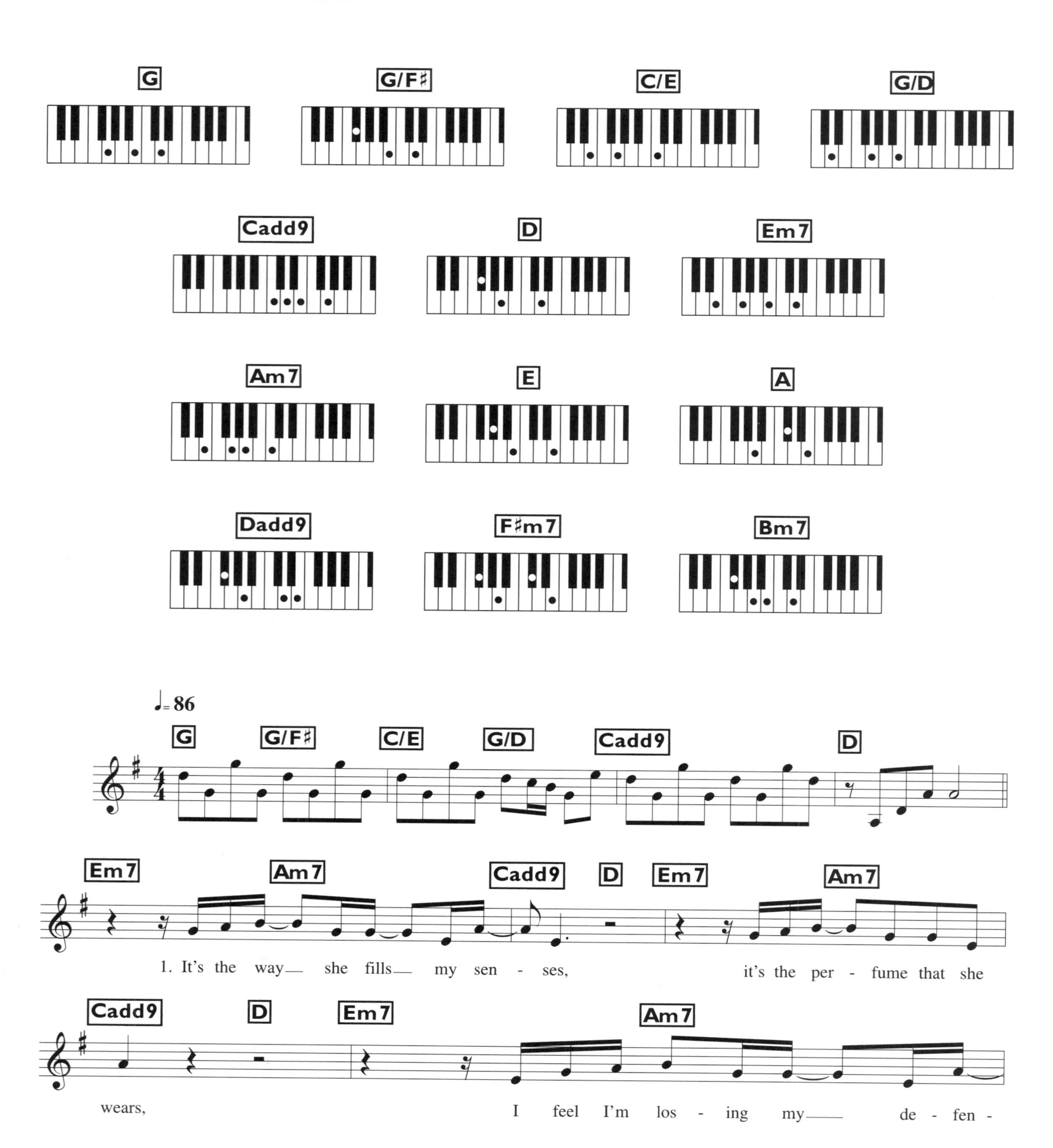

Cadd9 D Em7 Am7 Cadd9 D
- ces, to the co - lour of her hair, and ev -
Cadd9 G Am7 D
- 'ry lit - tle piece of her is right, just think -
Cadd9 G Am7 D
- ing a - bout her, takes me through the night. Ev - 'ry time we meet
1 2 3 4+
G D Cadd9 D
the pic - ture is com - plete, ev - 'ry time we touch,
G D Cadd9 D
the feel - ing is too much, she's all I ev - er need,
Em7 D Cadd9 G
to fall in love a - gain, I knew it from the ve -
1.
Am7 G Cadd9 G G/F♯ Cadd9 D
- ry start. She's the puz - zle of my heart.

Em7
Am7
Cadd9
D
2. It's the way she's al - ways smil - ing,

Em7
Am7
Cadd9
D
that makes me think she nev - er cries,

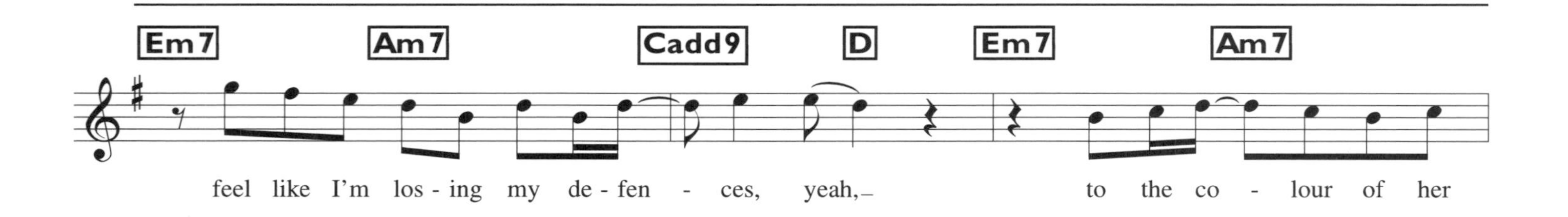
Em7
Am7
Cadd9
D
Em7
Am7
feel like I'm los - ing my de - fen - ces, yeah, to the co - lour of her

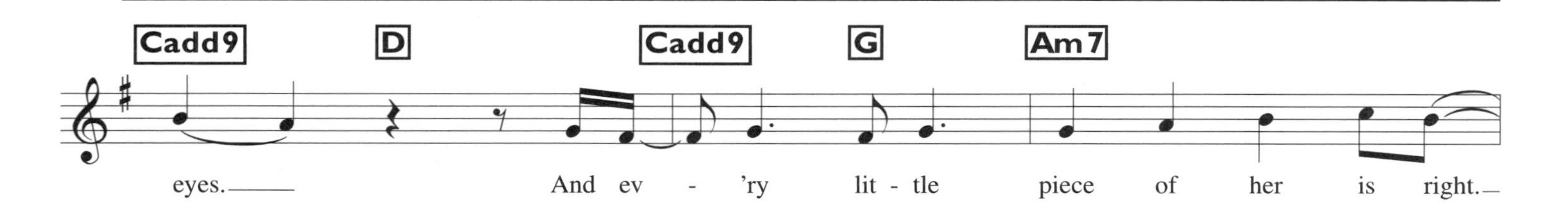
Cadd9
D
Cadd9
G
Am7
eyes. And ev - 'ry lit - tle piece of her is right.

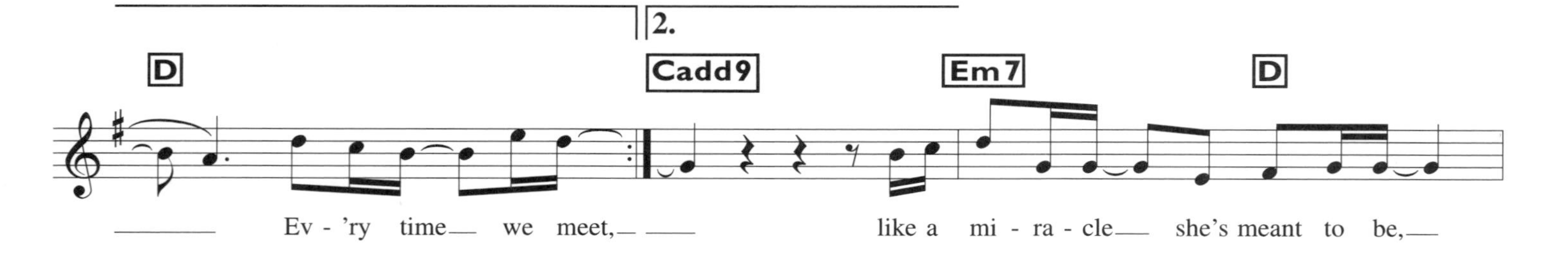
2.
D
Cadd9
Em7
D
Ev - 'ry time we meet, like a mi - ra - cle she's meant to be,

Cadd9
Em7
D
G
Cadd9
she be - came the light in - side of me, and I can

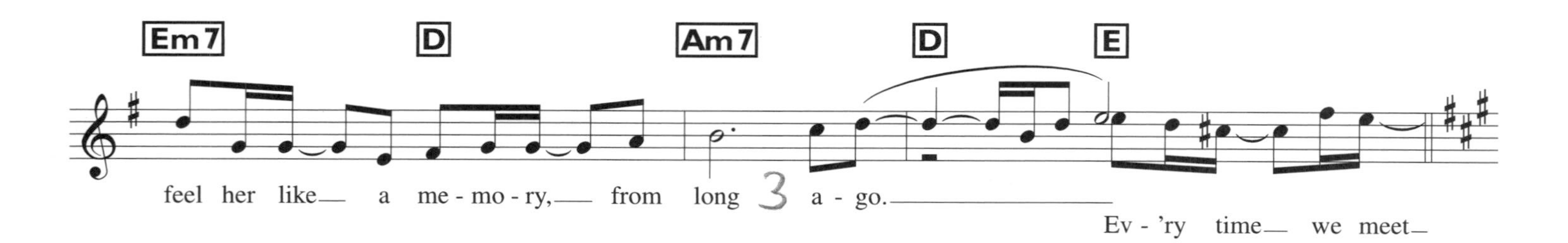
Em7
D
Am7
D
E
feel her like a me - mo - ry, from long a - go.
Ev - 'ry time we meet

A E Dadd9 E
the pic - ture is com - plete, ev - 'ry time we touch,
A E Dadd9 E
the feel - ing is too much. Ev - 'ry time we meet
A E Dadd9 E
the pic - ture is com - plete, ev - 'ry time we touch,
A E Dadd9 E
the feel - ing is too much. She's all I ev - er need
F♯m7 E Dadd9 A
to fall in love a - gain, I knew it from the ve -
Bm7 A Dadd9 E
rall.
- ry start, she's the puz - zle of my
A a tempo Dadd9 rall. E A
heart. Ooh, ooh, ooh, ooh.

15/3/02

DREAMS COME TRUE

Words & Music by Jörgen Elofsson, Per Magnusson & David Kreuger

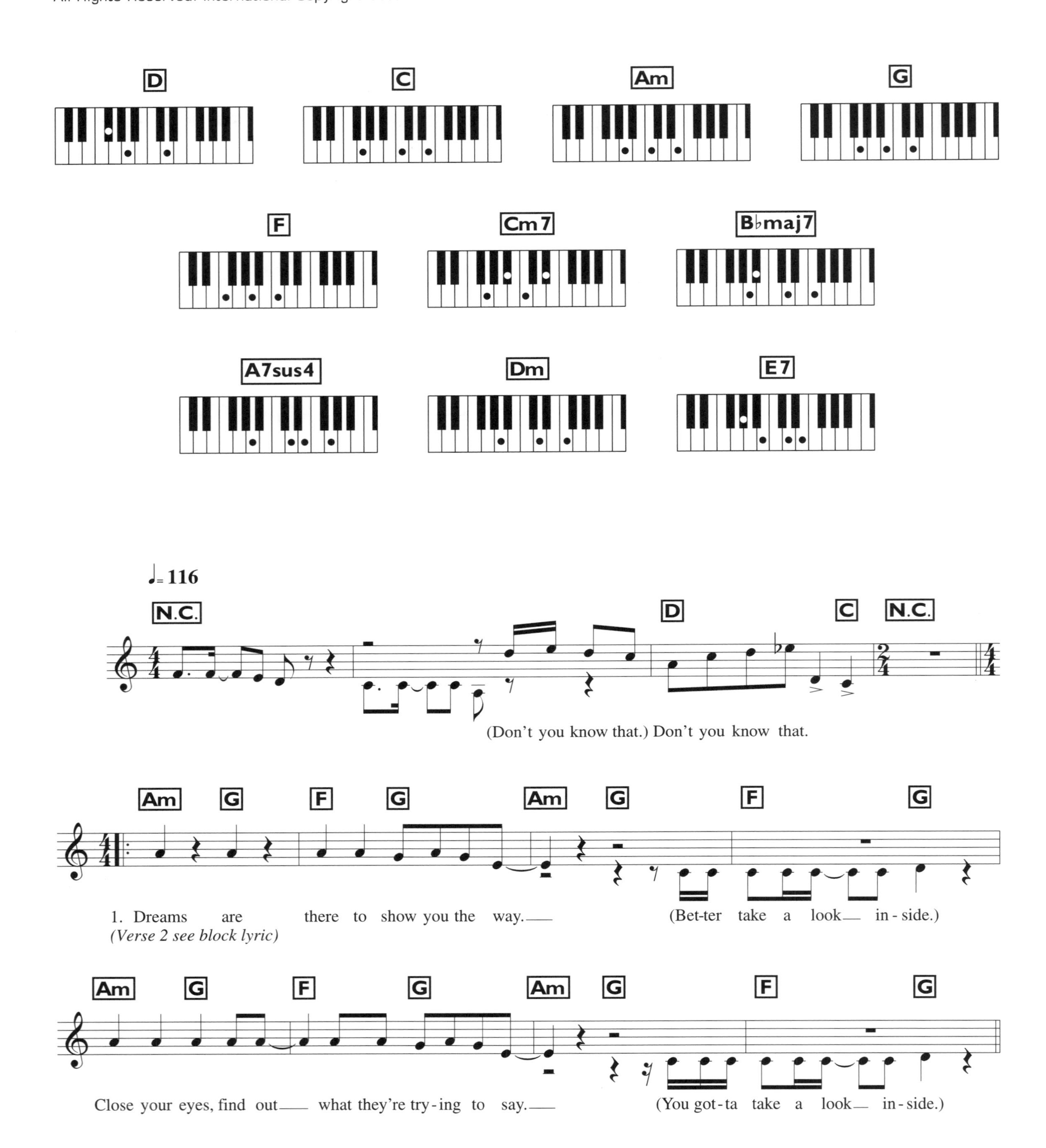

Cm7
B♭maj7
Cm7
B♭maj7
On - ly for a mi-nute, just to make a start, i - ma-gine what you wan-na see.

Cm7
B♭maj7
A7sus4
D
Wake him up, the wi-zard, sleep-ing in your heart, just i - ma-gine what you wan-na be. Don't you know that
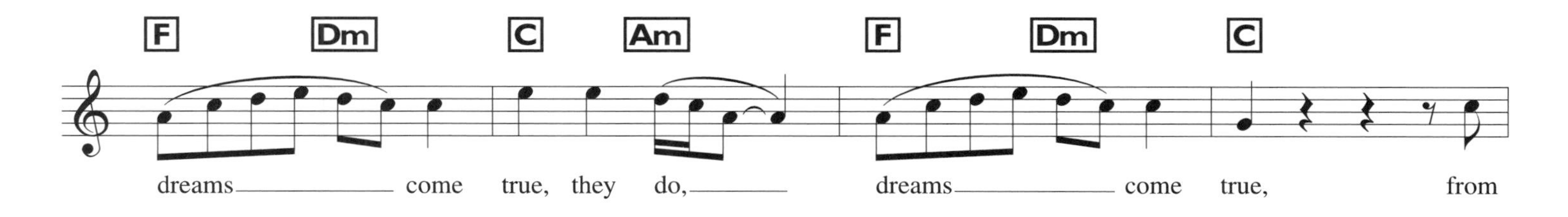
F
Dm
C
Am
F
Dm
C
dreams come true, they do, dreams come true, from

1.
F
Dm
C
Am
Dm
C
N.C.
all of us to all of you they do, don't you know that dreams come.
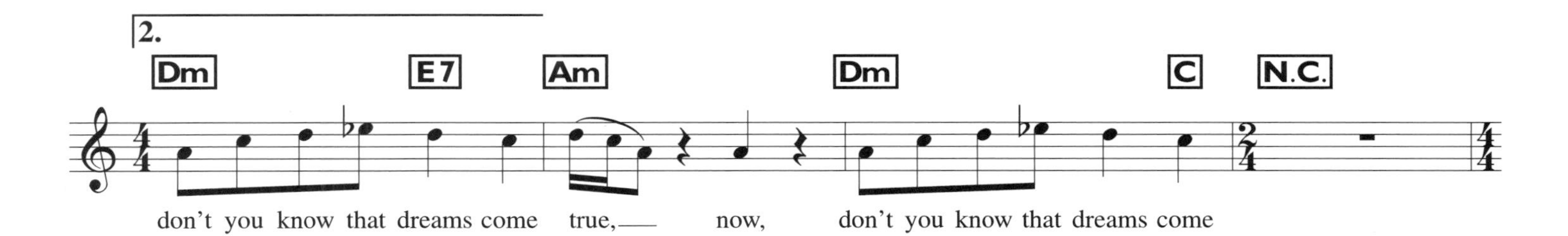
2.
Dm
E7
Am
Dm
C
N.C.
don't you know that dreams come true, now, don't you know that dreams come
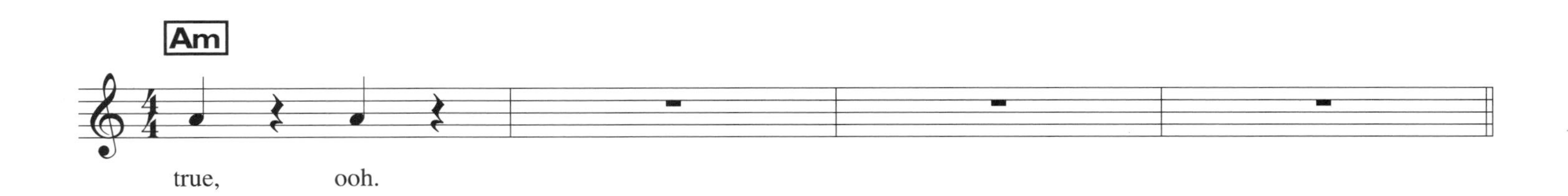
Am
true, ooh.
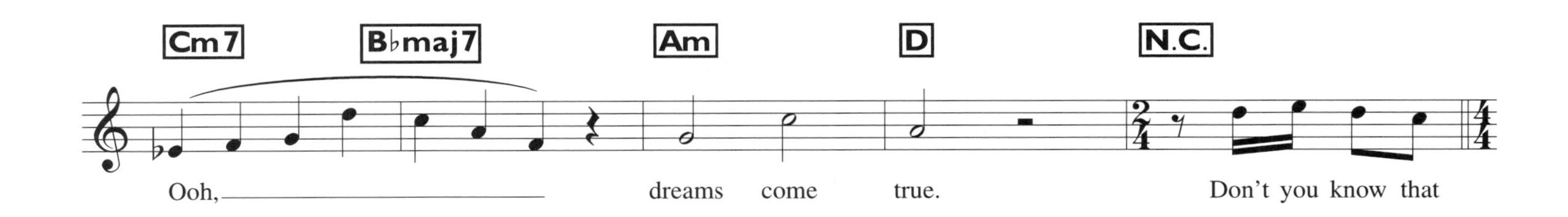
Cm7
B♭maj7
Am
D
N.C.
Ooh, dreams come true. Don't you know that

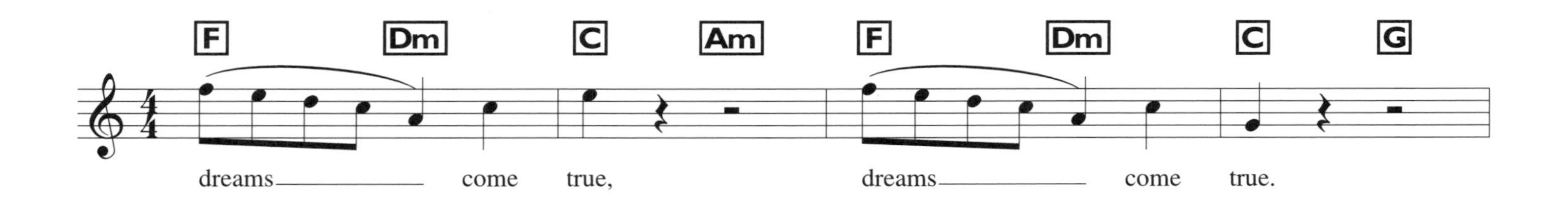

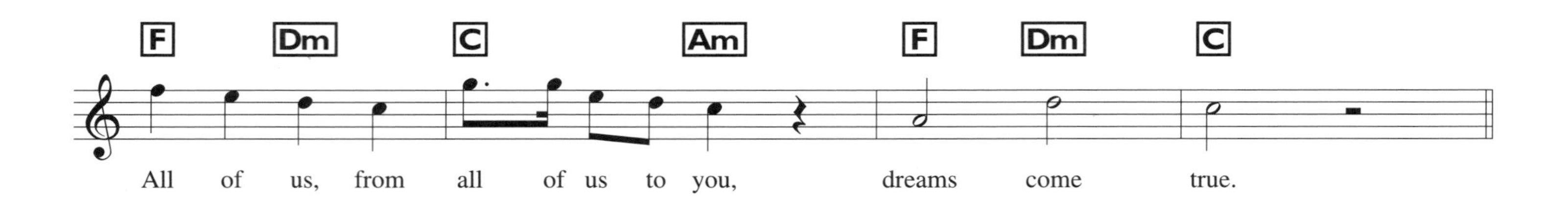

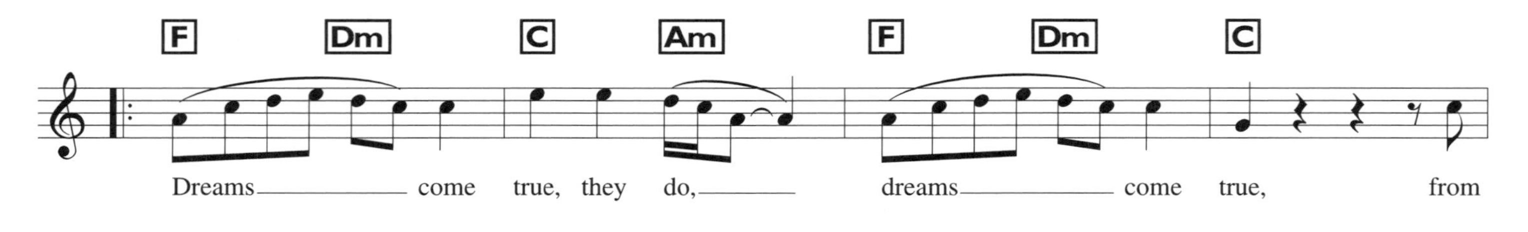

Verse 2:
True love is just a second away
(Better take a look inside.)
Make that magic rule, let the miracle stay
(You gotta take a look inside.)

Only for a minute, just to make a start
Imagine what you wanna see.
Only for a minute, it's not a fantasy
Just imagine what you wanna be.

NO PLACE THAT FAR

Words & Music by Sara Evans, Tom Shapiro & Tony Martin

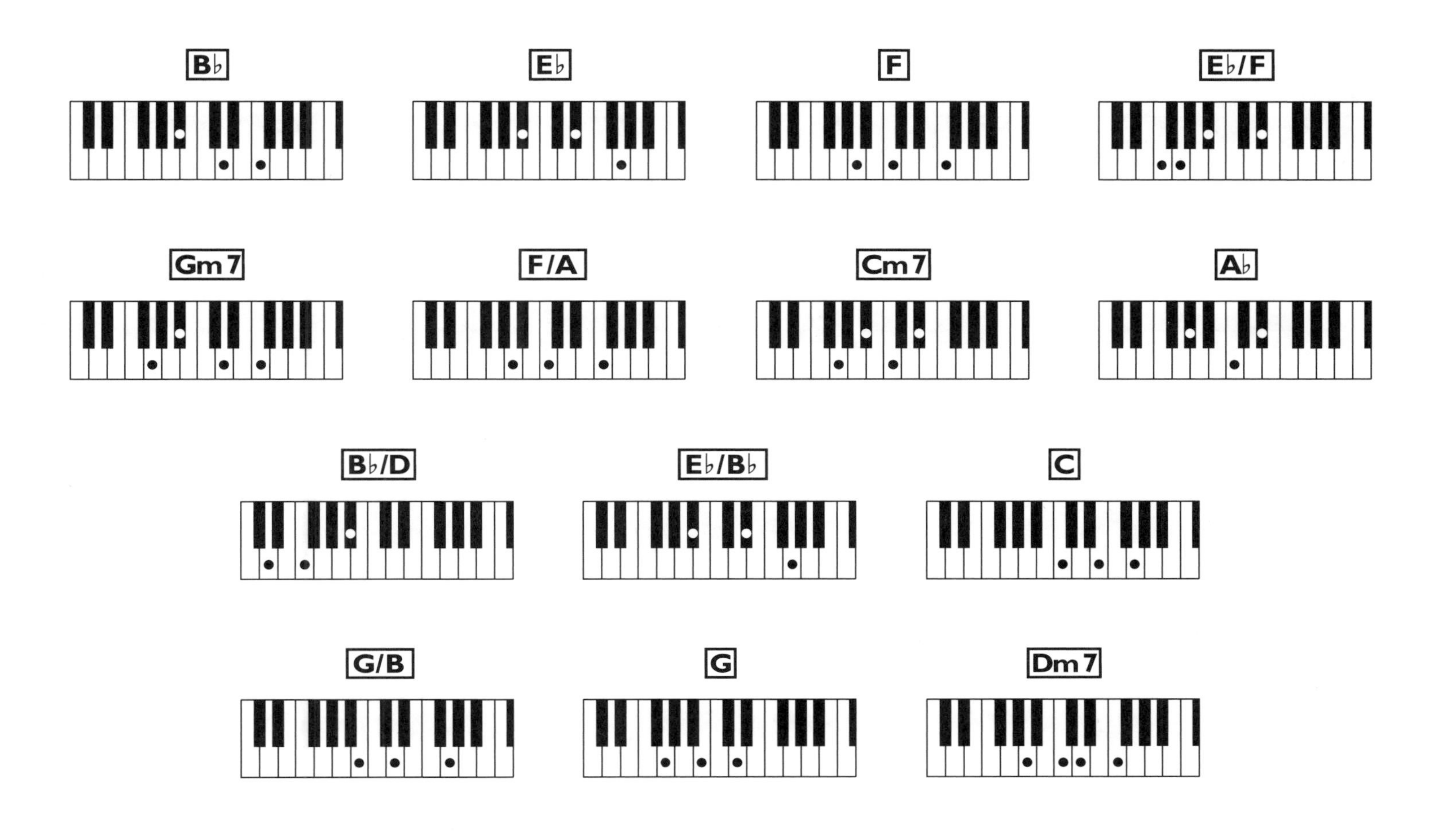

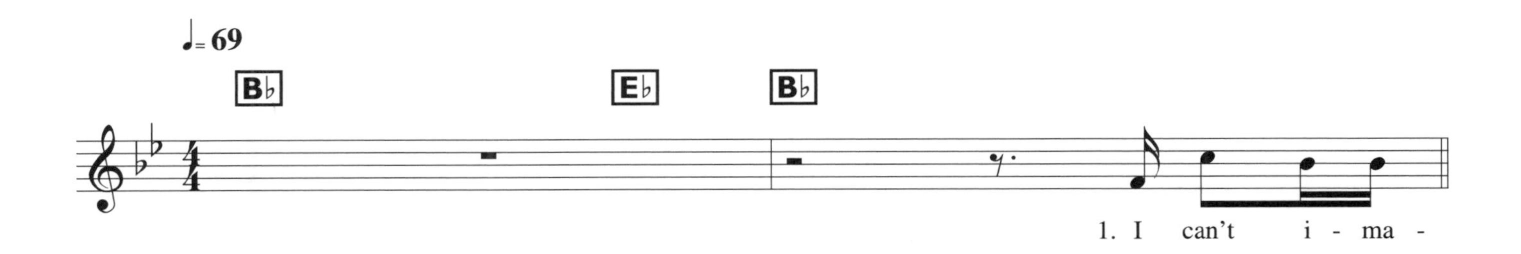

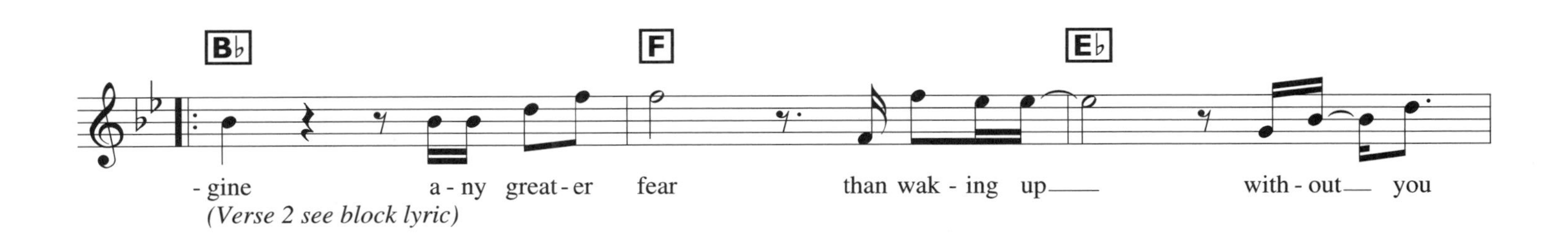

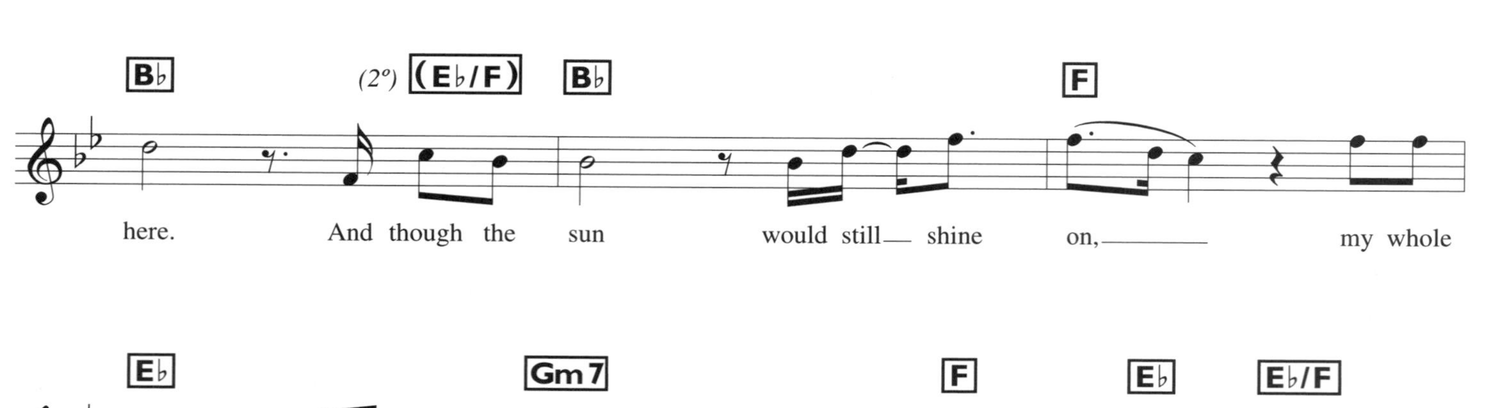
B♭ (2º) (E♭/F) B♭ F
here. And though the sun would still shine on, my whole

E♭ Gm7 F E♭ E♭/F
world would all be gone, but not for long. If I had to run,

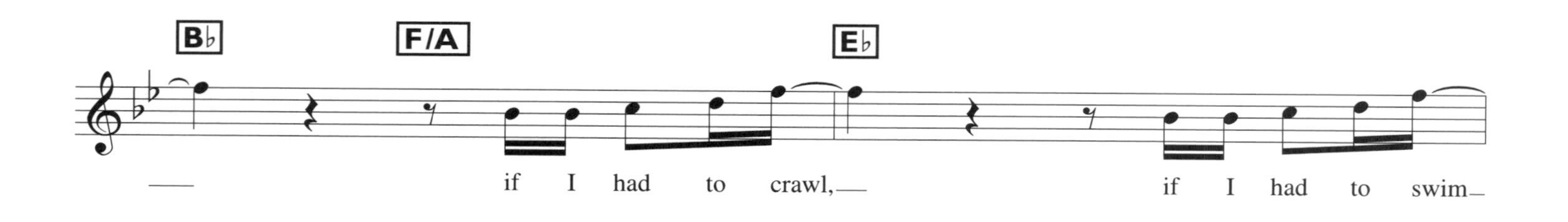
B♭ F/A E♭
if I had to crawl, if I had to swim

B♭ F
a hun - dred riv - ers, just to climb a thou - sand walls. Al-ways

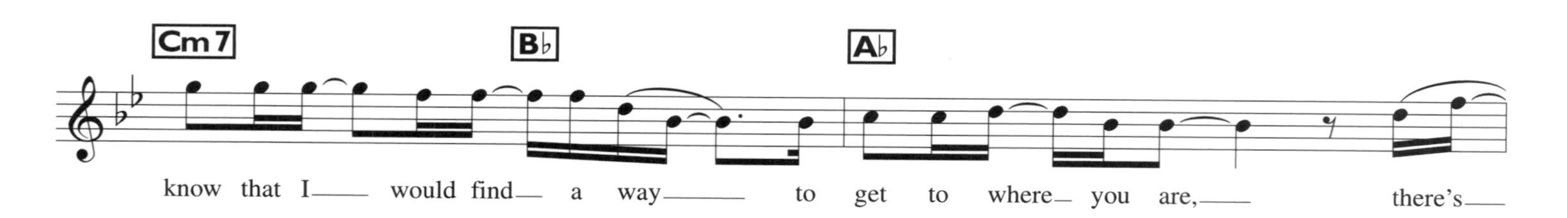
Cm7 B♭ A♭
know that I would find a way to get to where you are, there's

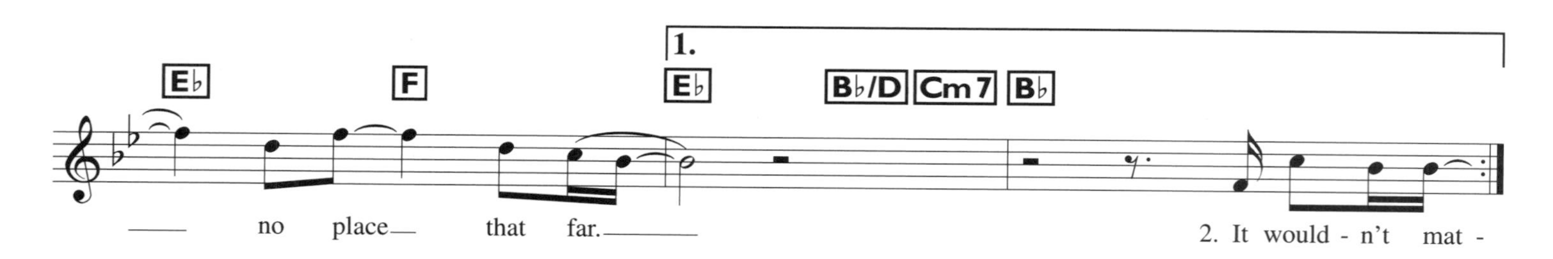
1.
E♭ F E♭ B♭/D Cm7 B♭
no place that far.
2. It would - n't mat -

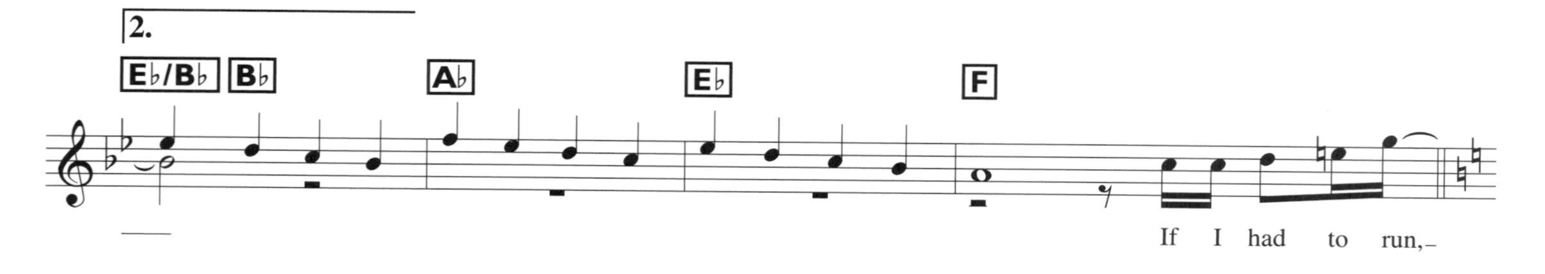
2.
E♭/B♭ B♭ A♭ E♭ F
If I had to run,

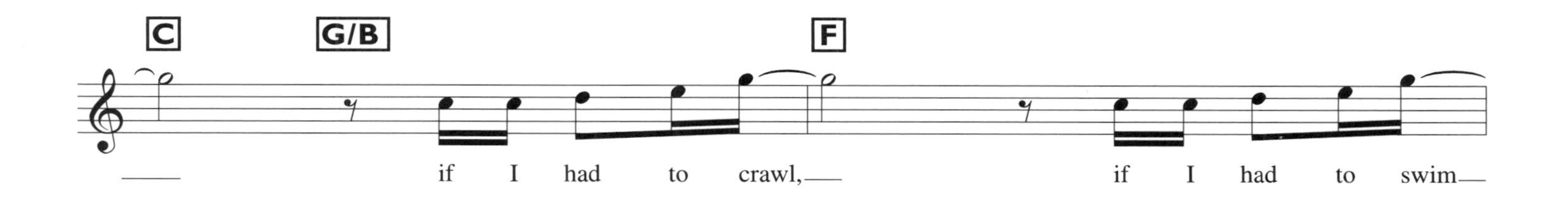

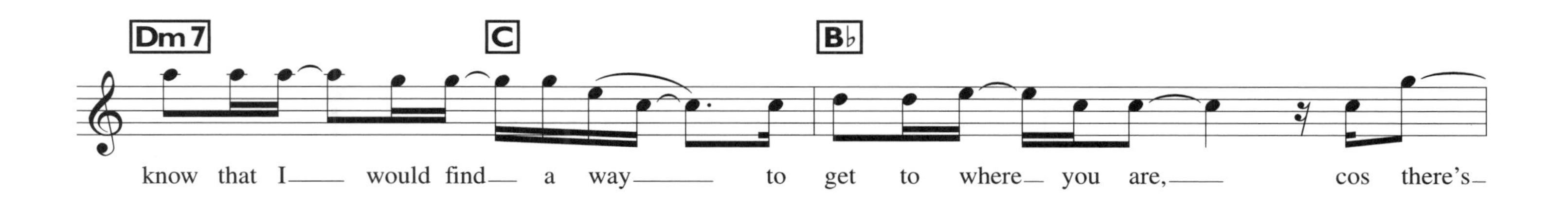

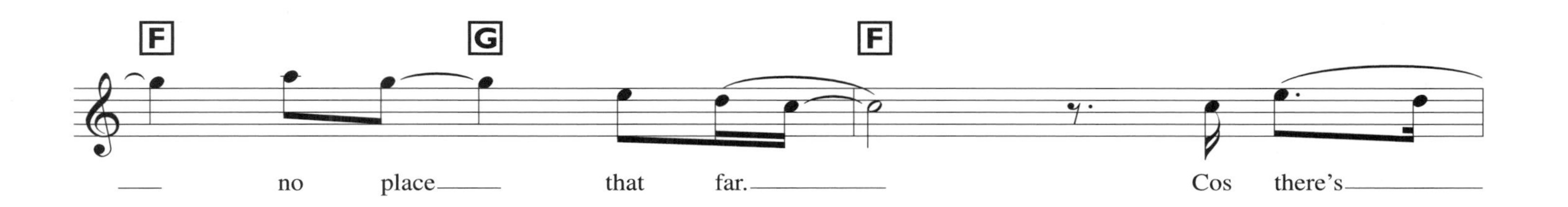

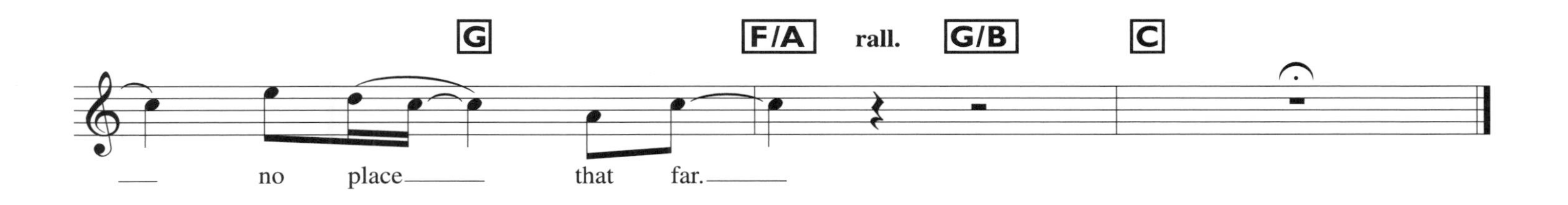

Verse 2:
It wouldn't matter why we're apart
Lonely mouths, two stubborn hearts.
Nothing short of God above
Could turn me away from your love.
I need you that much.

CLOSE YOUR EYES

Words & Music by Steve Mac & Wayne Hector

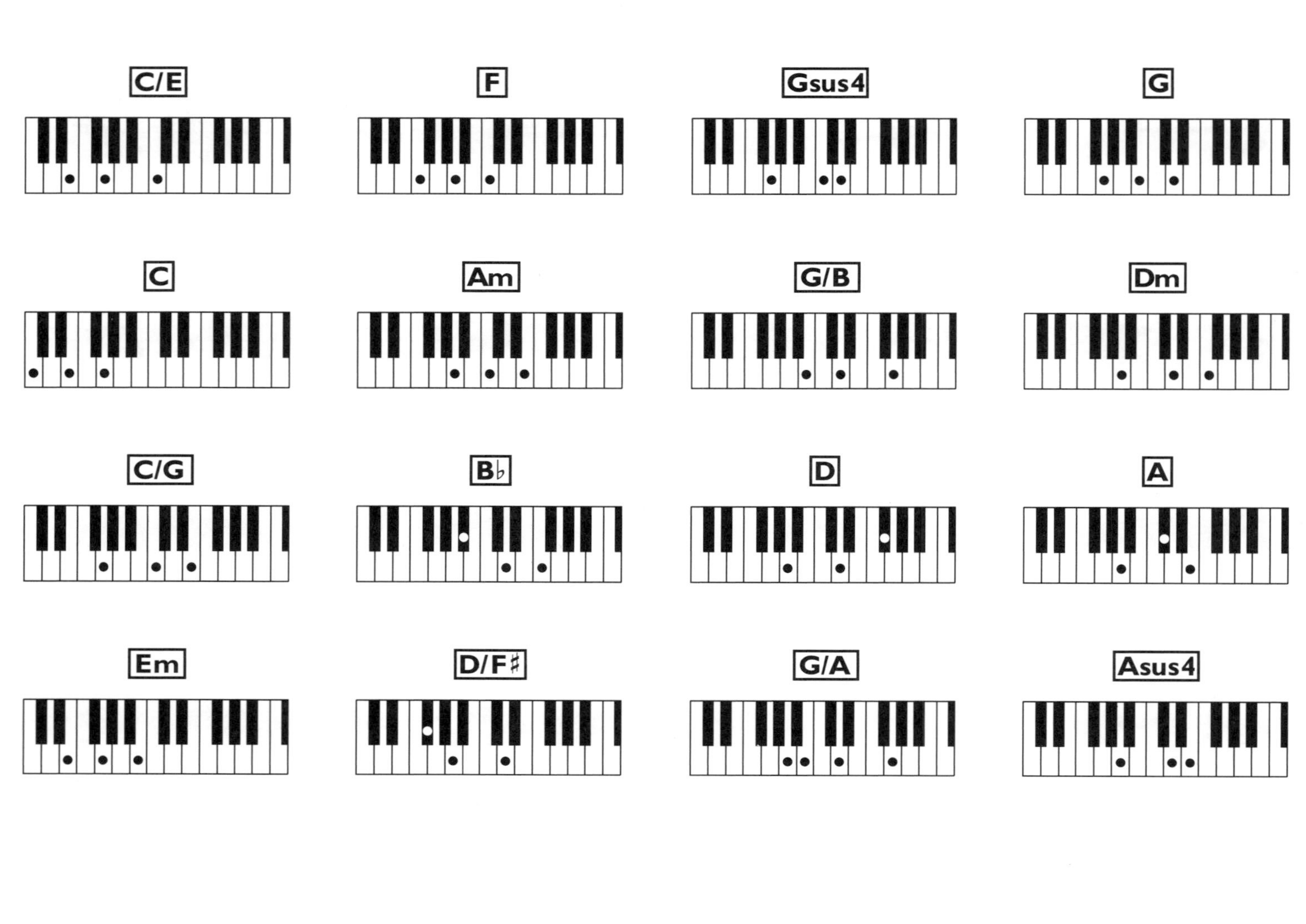

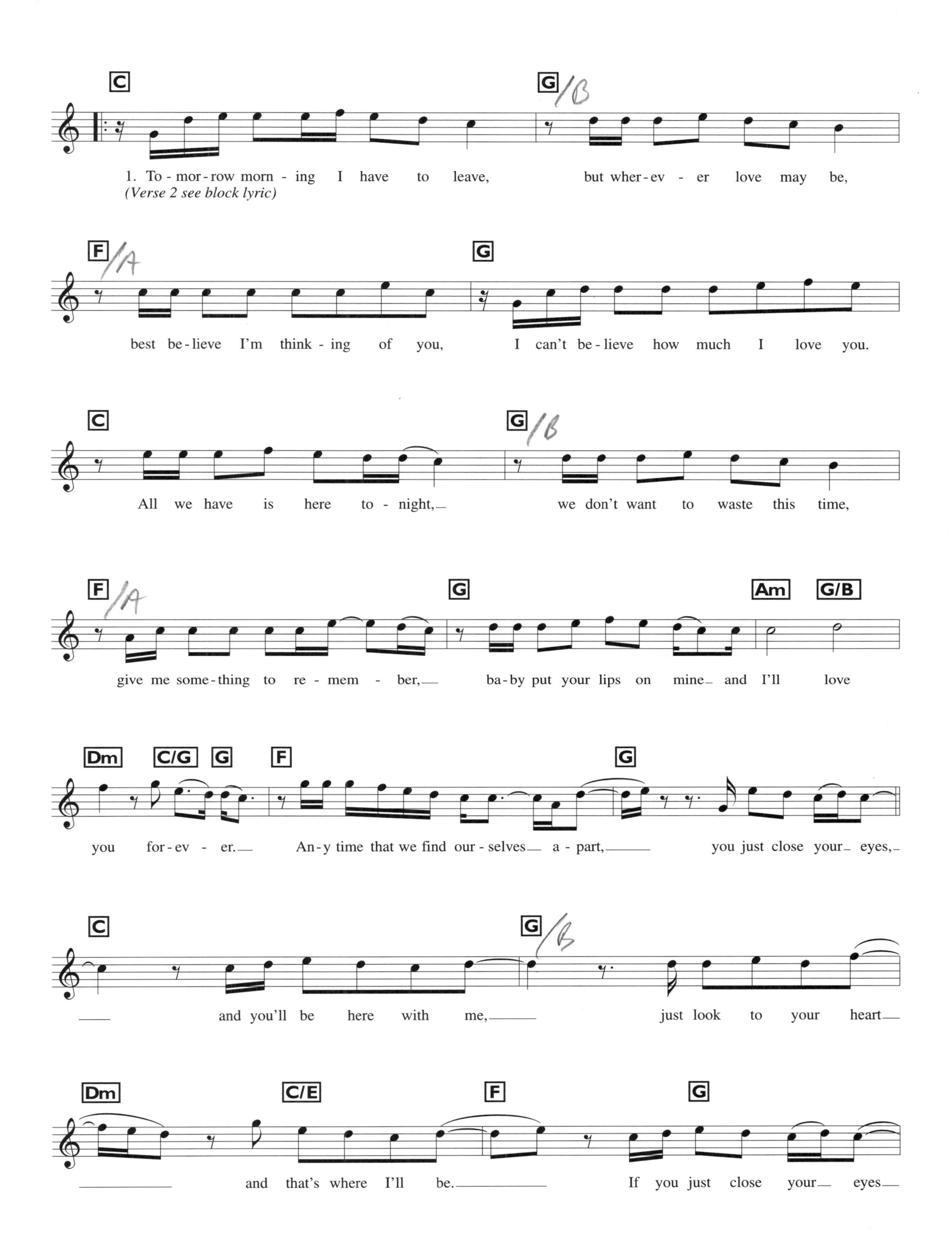
C
G/B
1. To - mor - row morn - ing I have to leave, but wher - ev - er love may be,
(Verse 2 see block lyric)
F/A
G
best be - lieve I'm think - ing of you, I can't be - lieve how much I love you.
C
G/B
All we have is here to - night, we don't want to waste this time,
F/A
G
Am
G/B
give me some - thing to re - mem - ber, ba - by put your lips on mine and I'll love
Dm
C/G
G
F
G
you for - ev - er. An - y time that we find our - selves a - part, you just close your eyes,
C
G/B
and you'll be here with me, just look to your heart
Dm
C/E
F
G
and that's where I'll be. If you just close your eyes

C
G
till you're drift - ing a - way,
you'll nev - er be too
F
G
1.
far from me,
if you close your eyes.
C/E
F
Gsus4
G
2.
if you close your
F
G
Am
G
F
eyes. Is there an - y-where that far? An - y time you're feel - ing low,
G
Am
G
C
F
is there an - y - where my love can - not reach? Oh no,
G
Am
B♭
I could be an - y-where on earth, it could be an - y-where I'll be,
G
oh ba - by if you wan - na see, you just close your eyes,

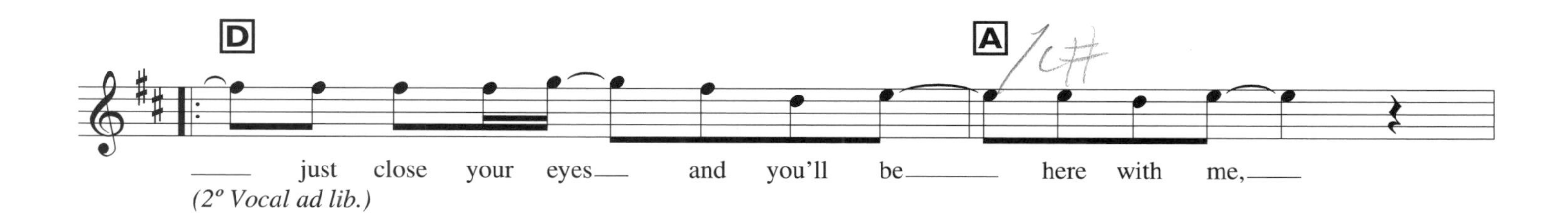

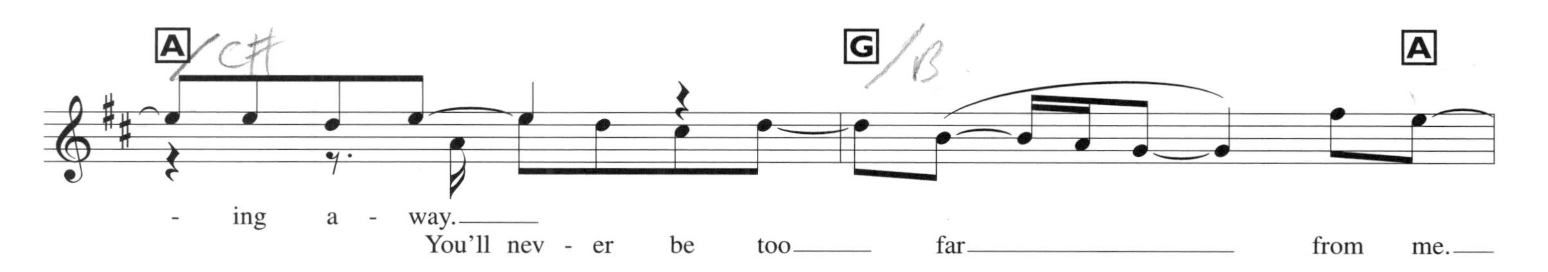

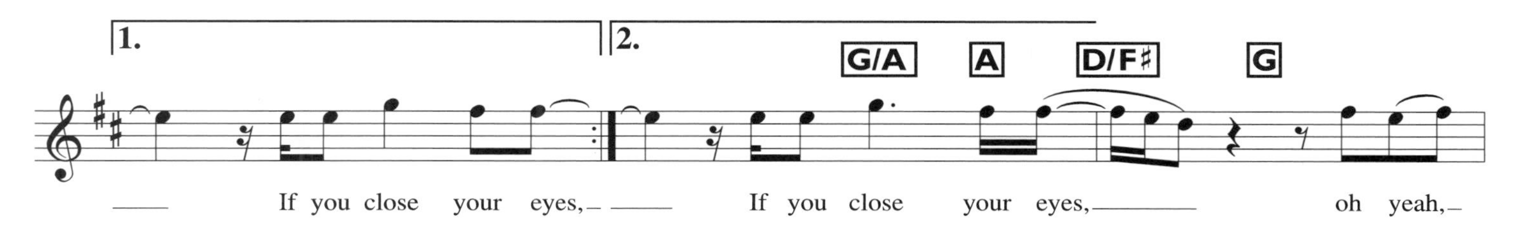

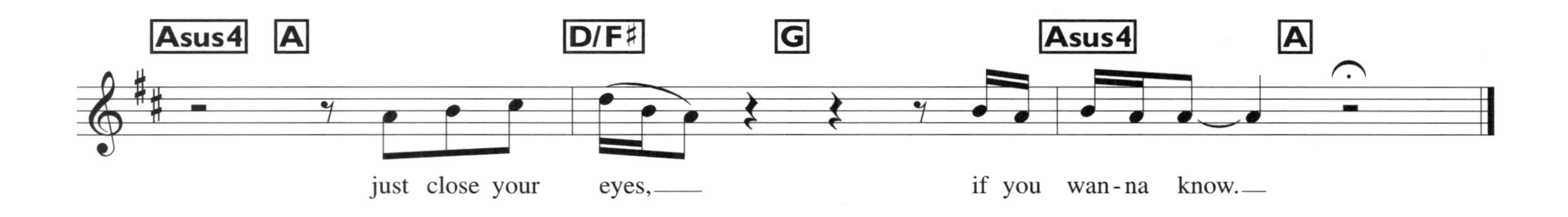

Verse 2:
I know I'm gonna see you again
But promise me that you won't forget
Cos as long as you remember
A part of us will be together.
So even when you're fast asleep
Look for me inside your dreams
Keep believing in what we're sharing
And even when I'm not there to tell you

I'll, I'll love you forever
Any time that I can't be where you are.

23/5/03

YOU MAKE ME FEEL

Words & Music by Niklas Jarl, Patric Jonsson & Max Martin

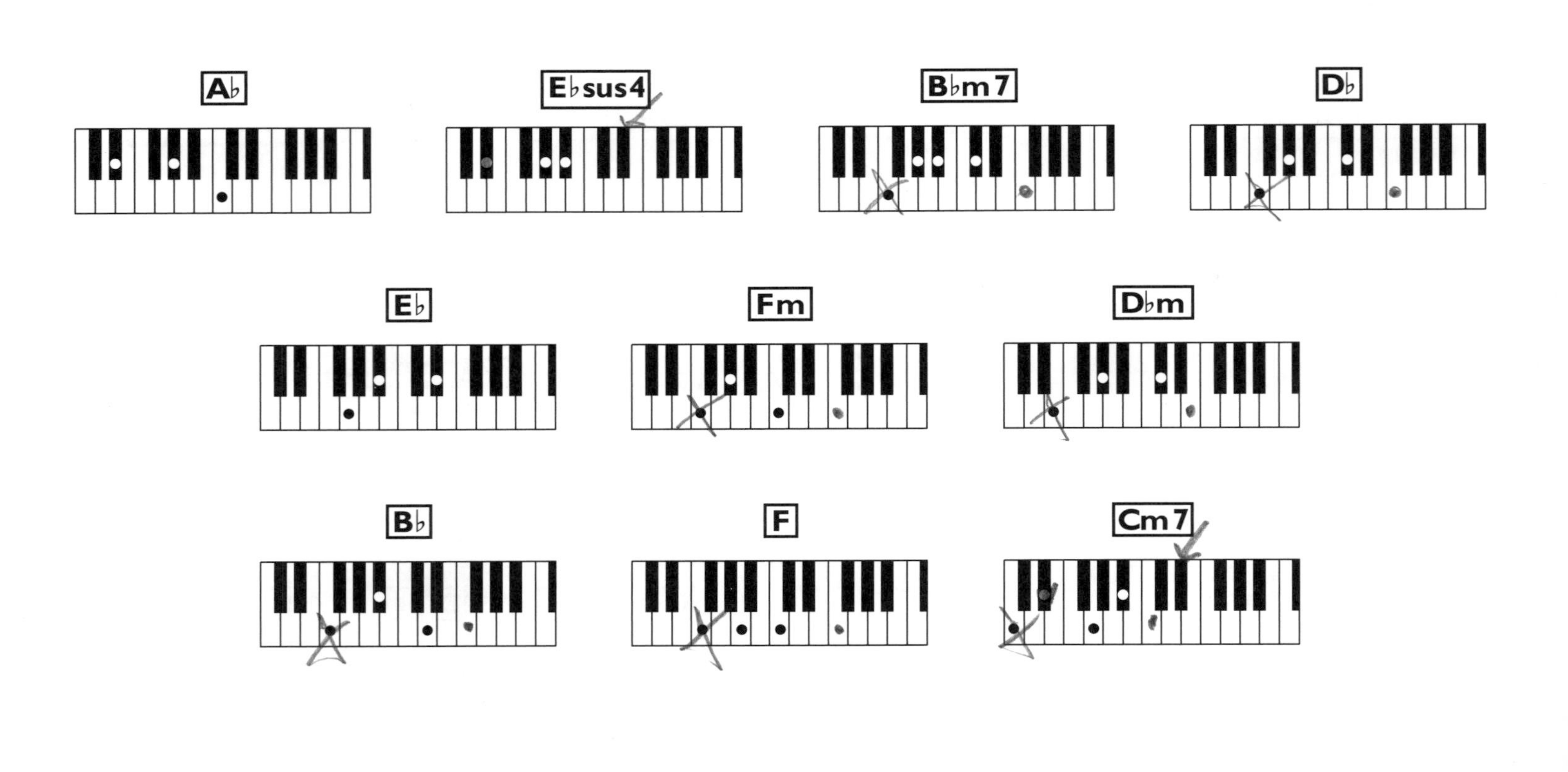

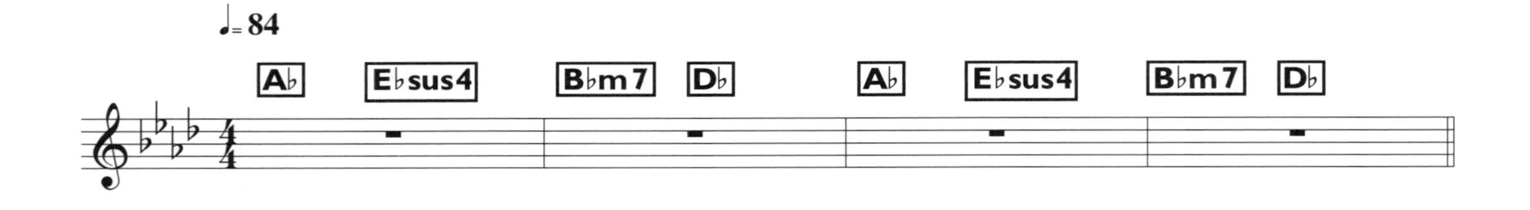

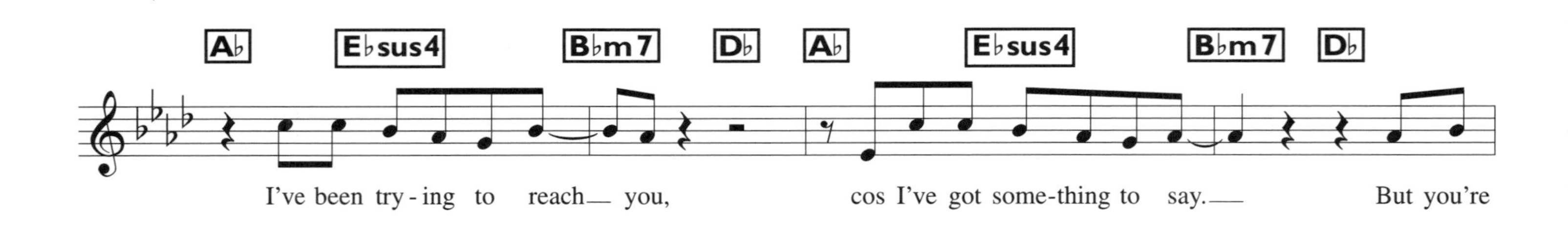

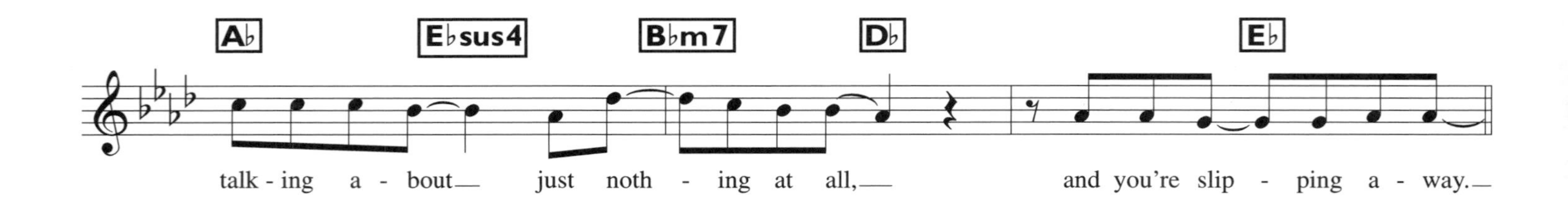

A♭ E♭sus4 B♭m7 D♭ A♭ E♭sus4 B♭m7 D♭
1. We were cry-ing to-geth - er, it was a long time a - go, be-fore you
(Verse 2 see block lyric)
A♭ E♭sus4 B♭m7 D♭ E♭ A♭
walk out that door and leave me this way, just hear what I say.
A♭ E♭ Fm D♭ A♭ E♭
You make me feel, you make me real,
B♭m7 D♭ A♭ E♭ B♭m7 D♭
for the rest of my days in so ma - ny ways,
1.
E♭ A♭ E♭sus4 B♭m7 D♭
you make me feel.
2.
D♭ E♭
you make me feel,
B♭m7 A♭ E♭ B♭m7
ten thou-sand light years a - way from you, keep think - ing
Fm E♭ B♭m7 Fm E♭
may - be it's time to let go, but by the end of the day I still want

Verse 2:
I've been trying to leave you
Why should we go on like this?
But my heart can't breathe when I hear you say
It's better this way.

LONELINESS KNOWS ME BY NAME

Words & Music by Alexandra

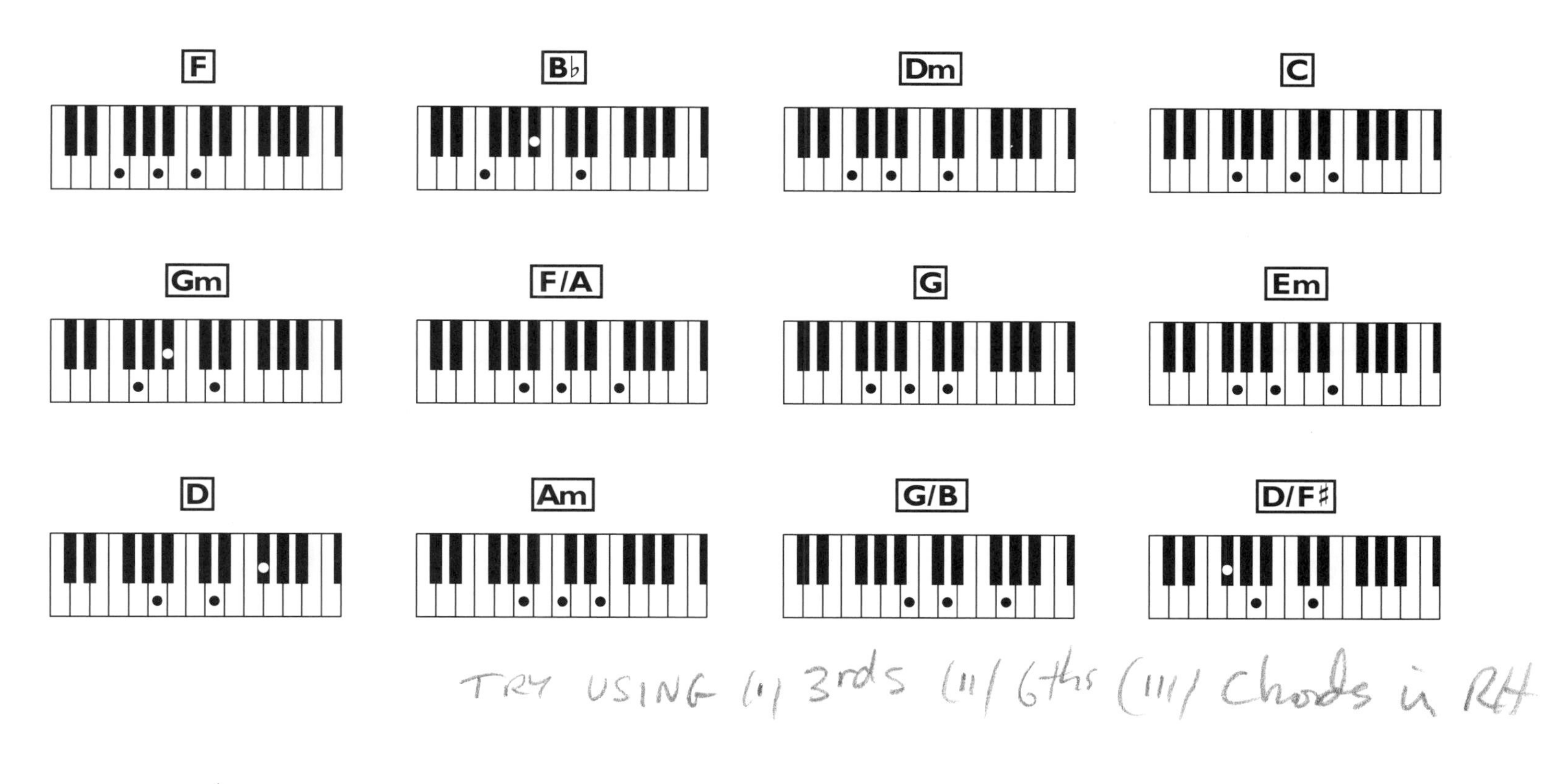

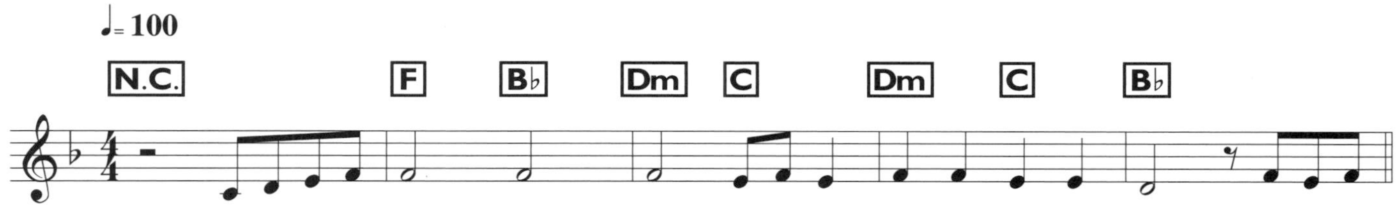

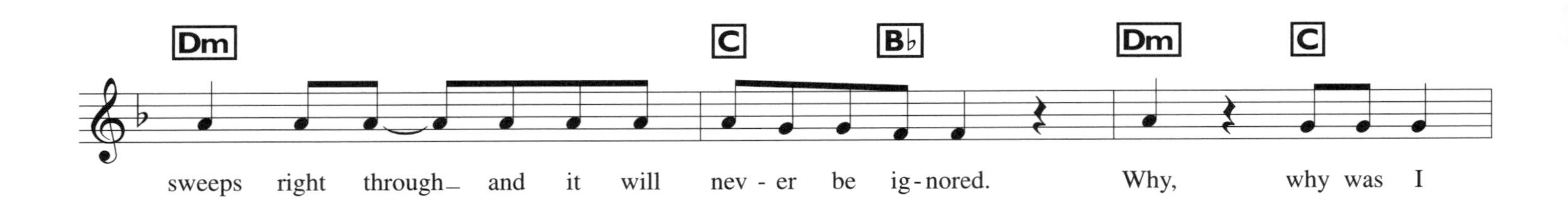
Dm C B♭ Dm C
sweeps right through_ and it will nev - er be ig - nored. Why, why was I

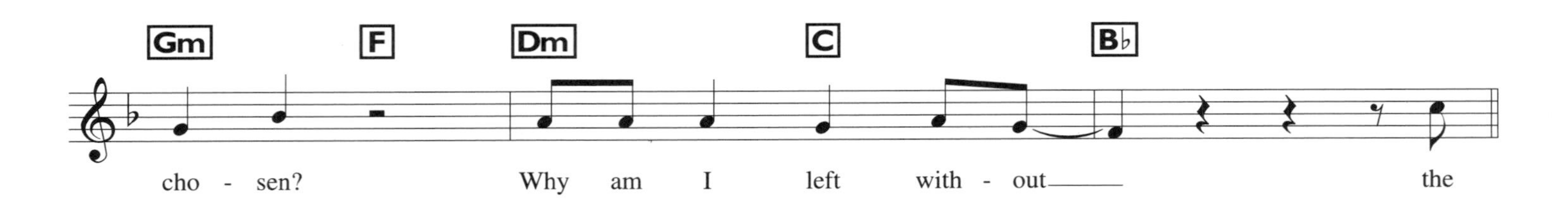
Gm F Dm C B♭
cho - sen? Why am I left with - out___ the

F B♭ Dm C F Gm F/A B♭
love of my life, the love that I need, the love that they say is in life___ for free?_ The

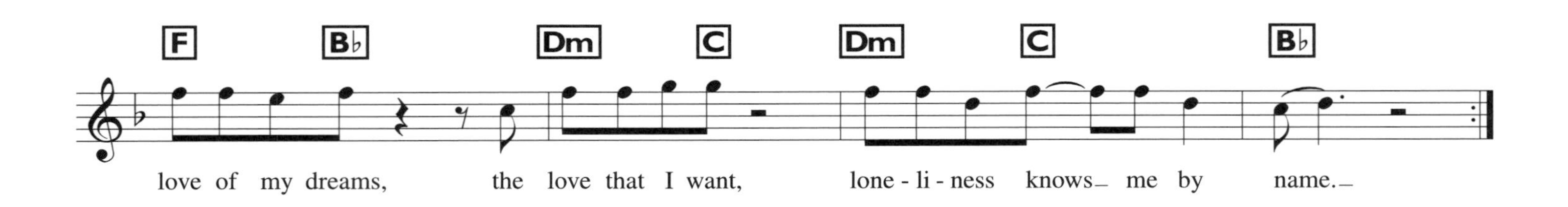
F B♭ Dm C Dm C B♭
love of my dreams, the love that I want, lone - li - ness knows_ me by name._

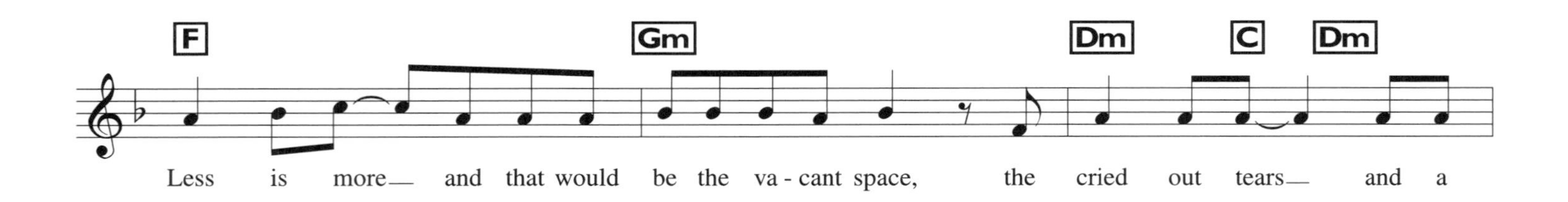
F Gm Dm C Dm
Less is more_ and that would be the va - cant space, the cried out tears_ and a

C B♭ F B♭
nev - er end - ing maze. Oh___ I have found_ what on - ly lone - li - ness pro-vides, a

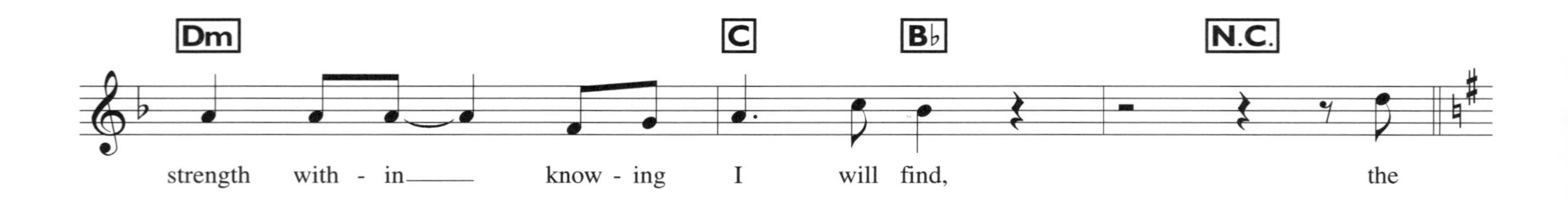
Dm C B♭ N.C.
strength with - in___ know - ing I will find, the

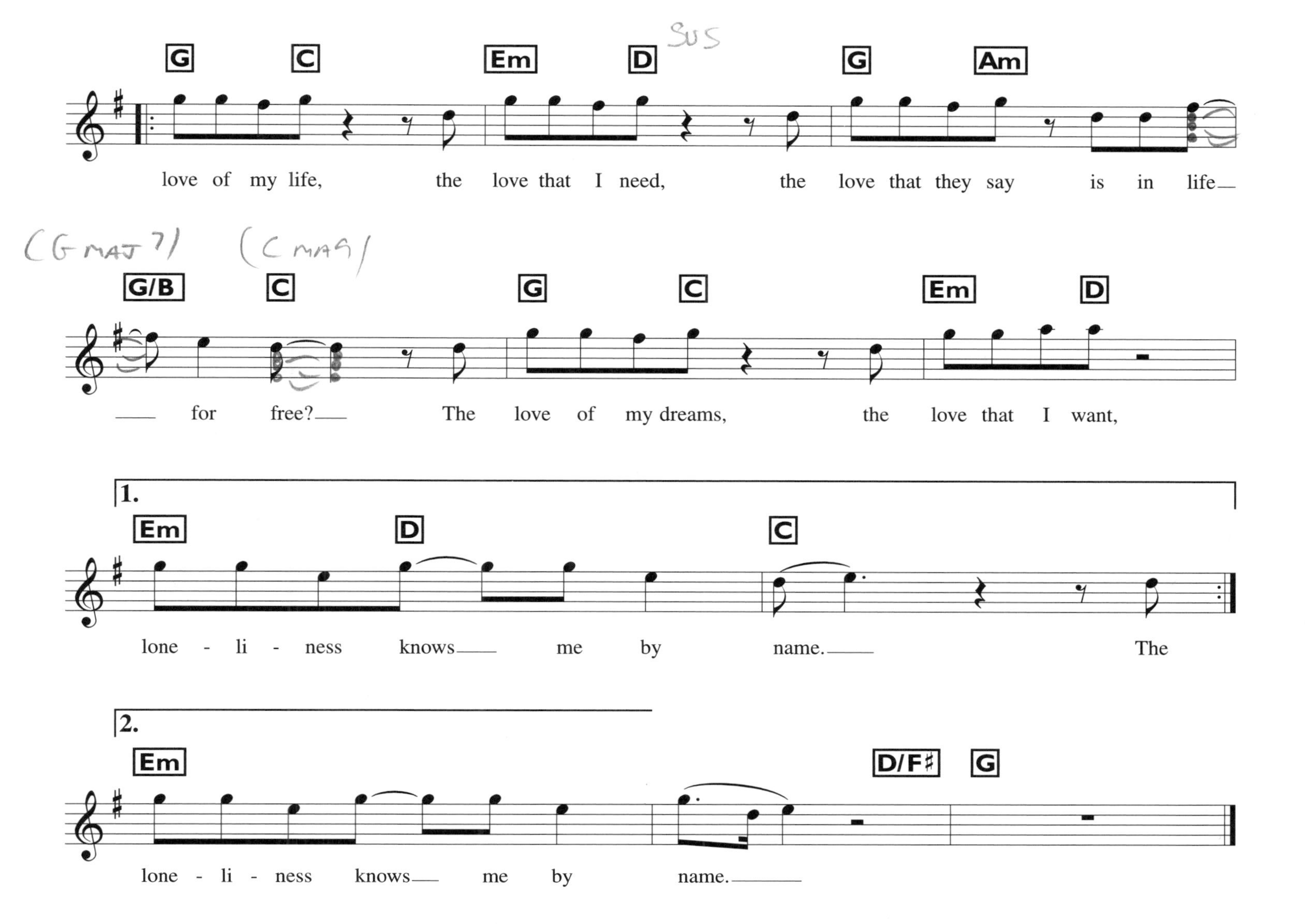

Verse 2:
Loneliness knows everything I keep inside
My endless thoughts in the silence of the night.
Loneliness is the one who made me see
Ain't nobody else who can make a change but me.

Why, why was I chosen?
Why am I left without

The love of my life *etc.*

EVERY LITTLE THING YOU DO

Words & Music by Steve Mac & Wayne Hector

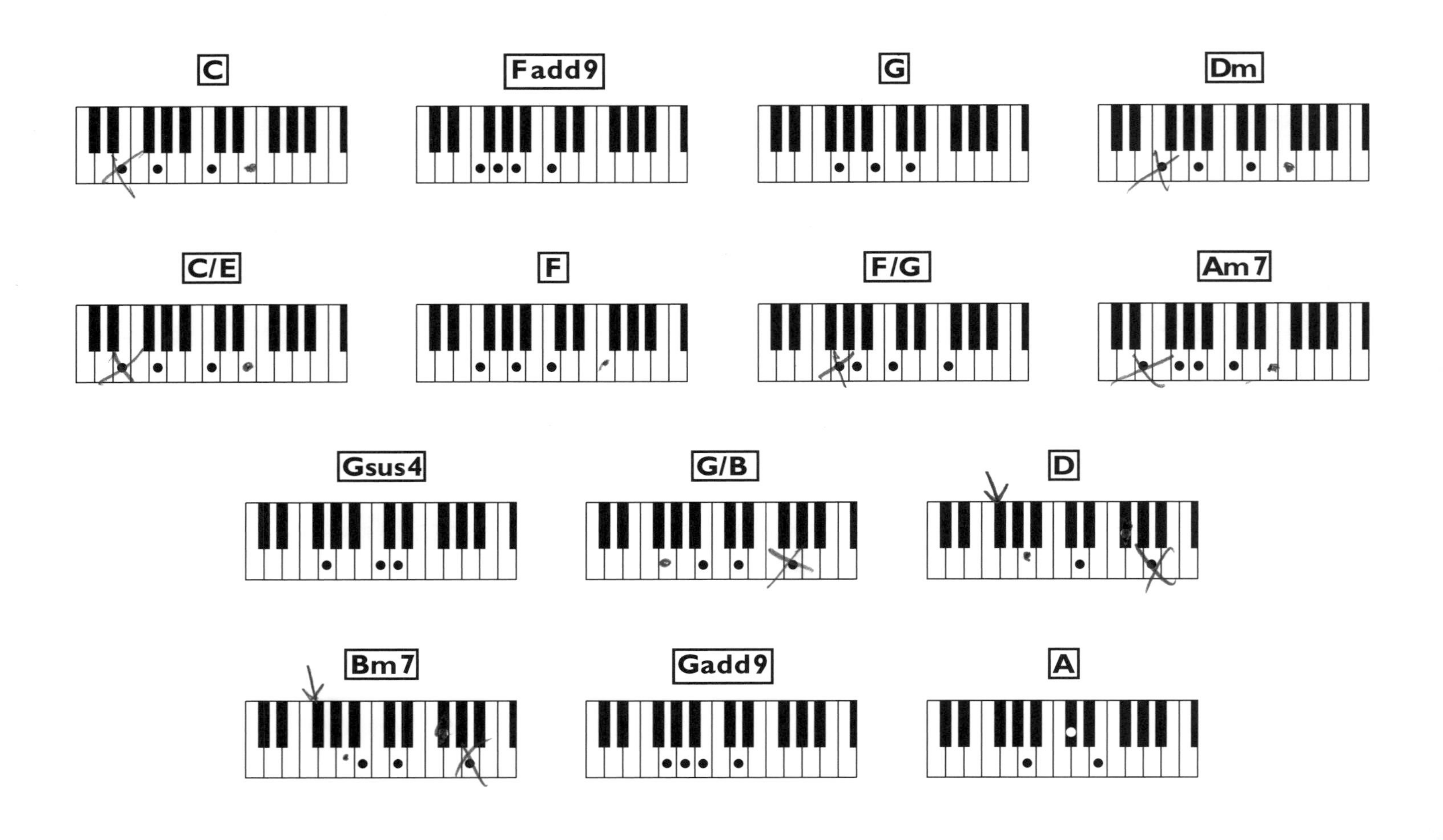

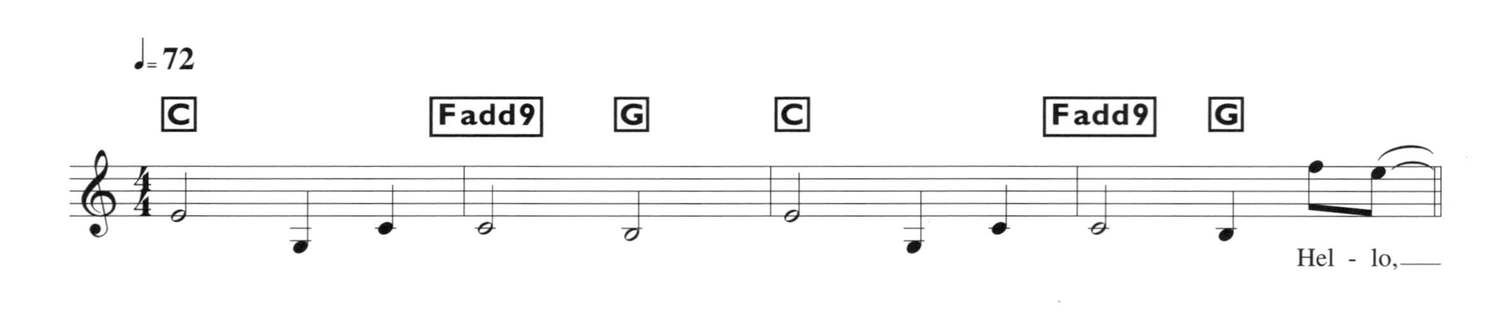

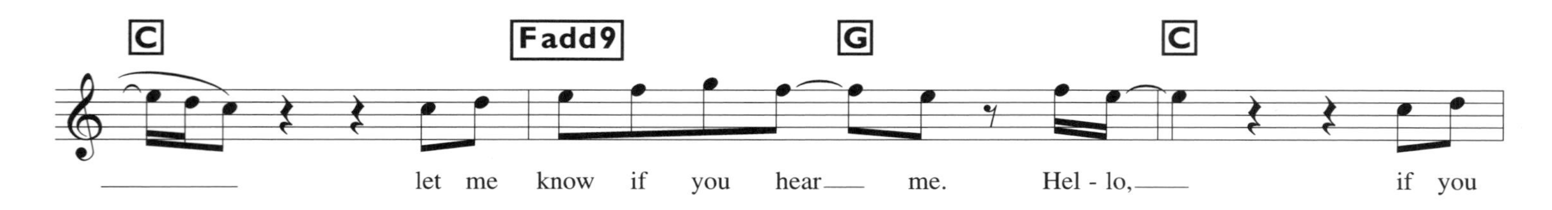

Fadd9 G Dm C/E F
want to be near, let me know and I'll nev - er let you go. 1. Hey love,

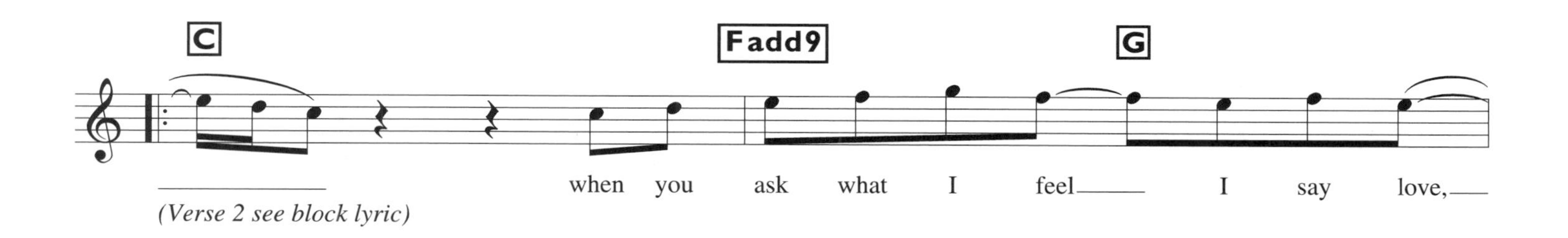
C Fadd9 G
when you ask what I feel I say love,
(Verse 2 see block lyric)

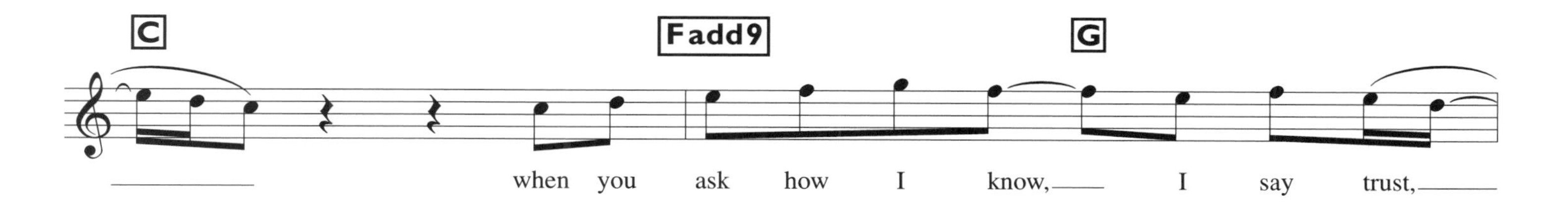
C Fadd9 G
when you ask how I know, I say trust,

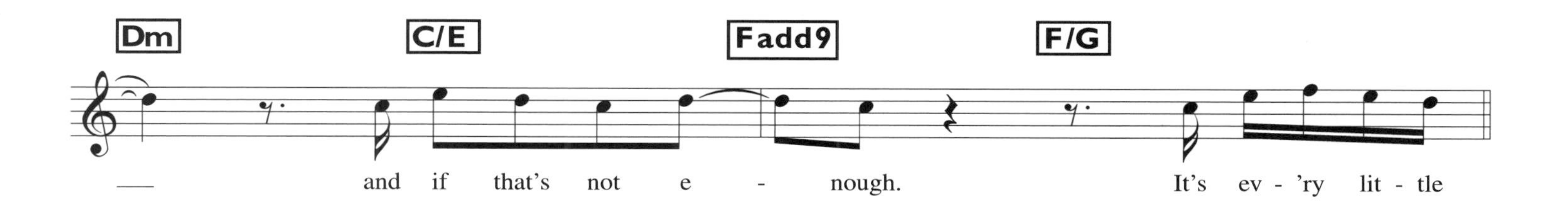
Dm C/E Fadd9 F/G
and if that's not e - nough. It's ev - 'ry lit - tle

C Am7
thing you do that makes me fall in love with you, there is - n't a way

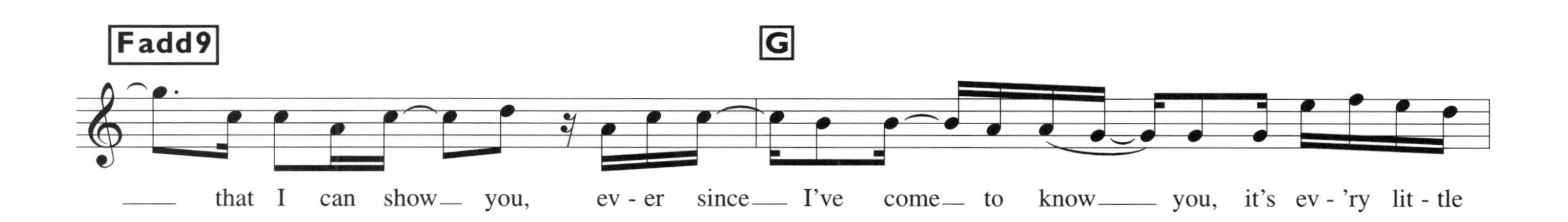
Fadd9 G
that I can show you, ev - er since I've come to know you, it's ev - 'ry lit - tle

C Am7
thing you say that makes me wan - na feel this way, there's not a thing

Fadd9
G
1.
that I can point to, cos it's ev - 'ry lit - tle thing you do.
2. Don't ask
2.
Fadd9
Gsus4
Am7
Is it your smile or your laugh or your heart? Does it real - ly mat-ter why I love you?
Fadd9
Gsus4
Am7
An - y - where there's a crowd, you stand out. Can't you see why they can't ig - nore you?
Fadd9
Gsus4
Am7
G/B
C
If you wan-na know why I can't let go, let me ex - plain to you that ev - 'ry lit - tle
Dm
C/E
F
G
N.C.
dream comes true with ev - 'ry lit - tle thing you do. It's ev - 'ry lit - tle
D
Bm7
thing you do that makes me fall in love with you, there is - n't a way
Gadd9
A
that I can show you, ev - er since I've come to know you, it's ev - 'ry lit - tle

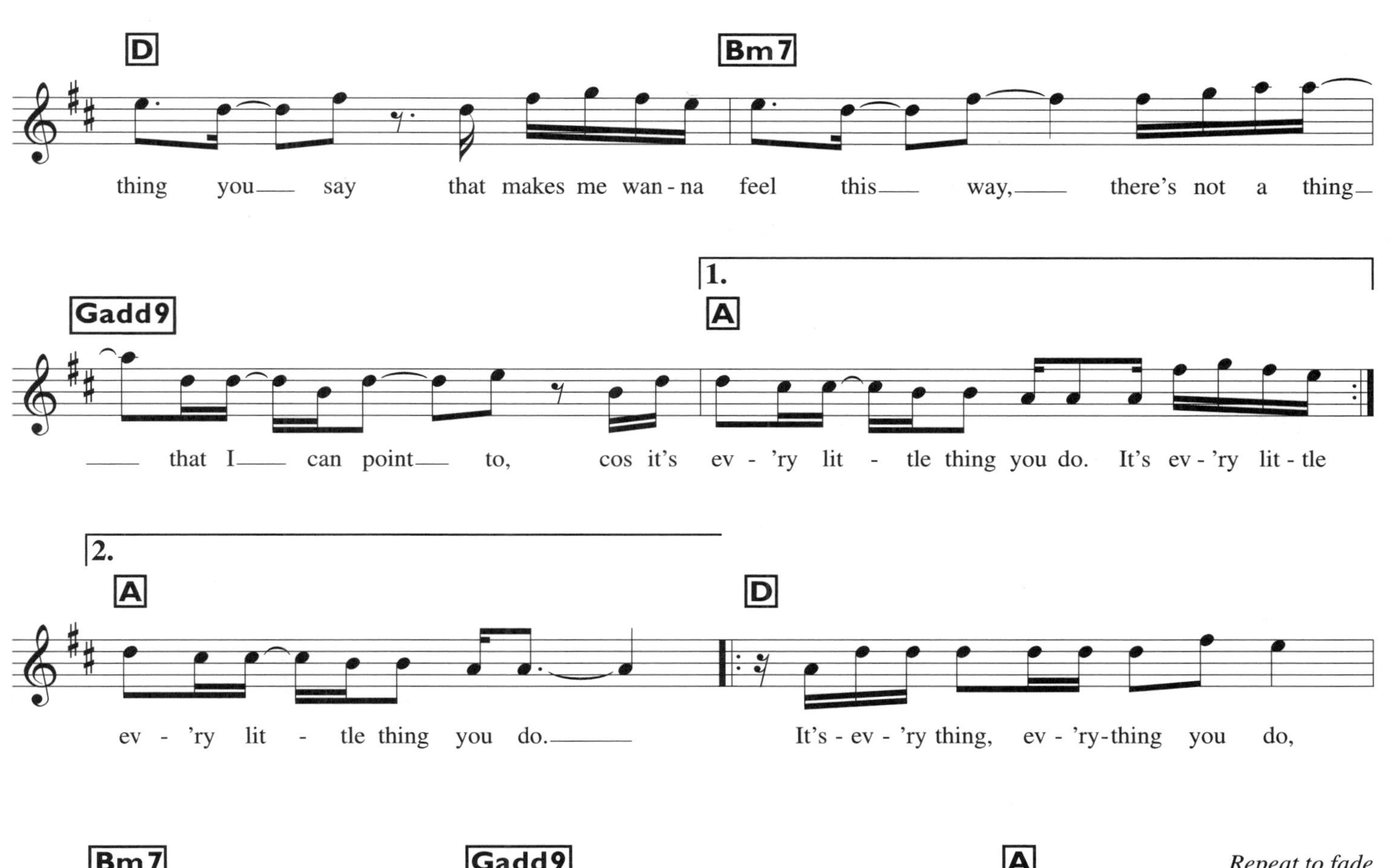

Verse 2:
Don't ask why
Let's just feel what we feel
Cos sometimes
It's the secret that keeps it alive.
But if you need a reason why.

It's ev'ry little thing *etc.*

FRAGILE HEART

Words & Music by Bryan McFadden, Kian Egan & Shane Filan

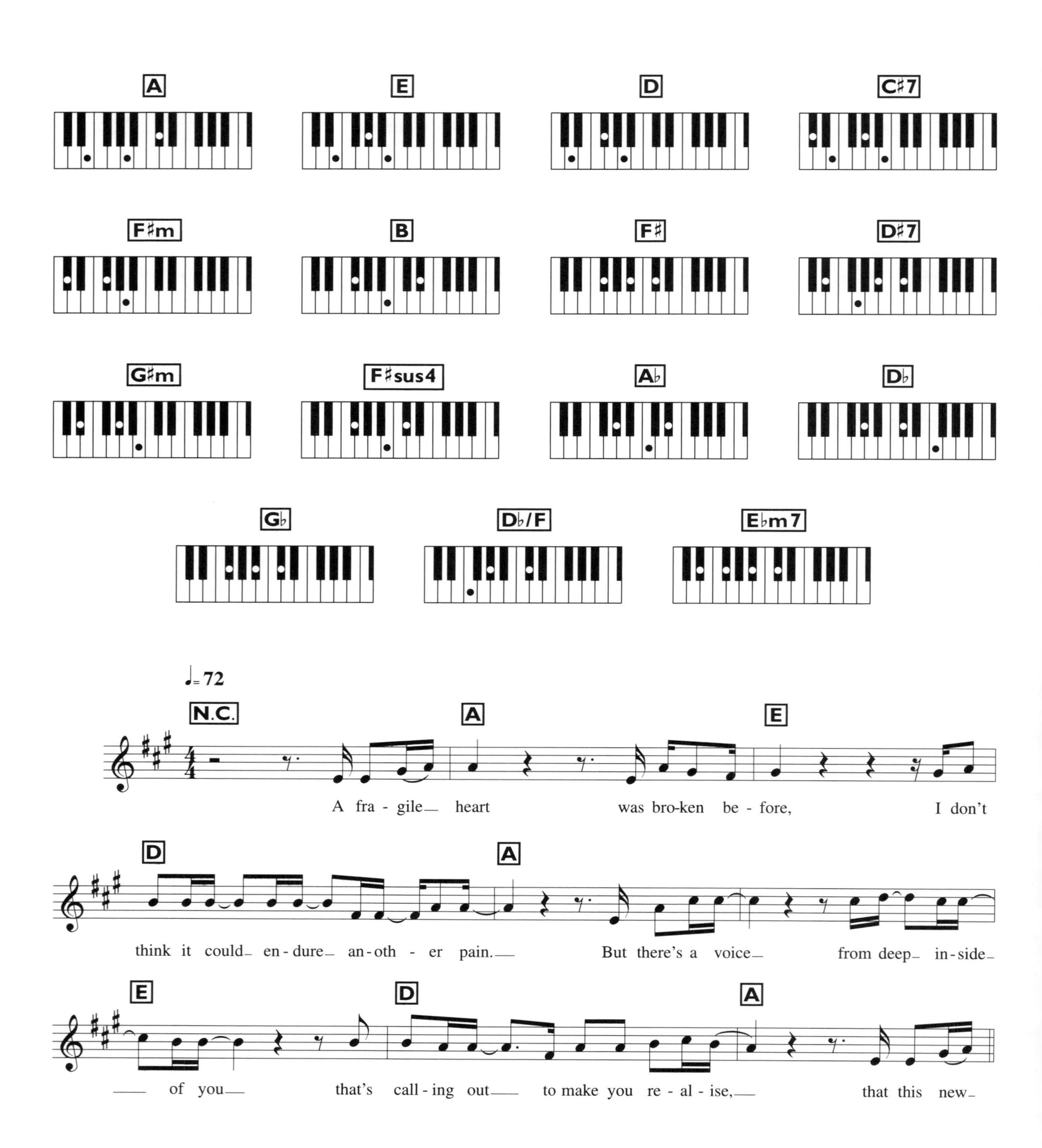

A
E
D
bond gives in - spi - ra - tion to all that feel, no love ap - peal no more.

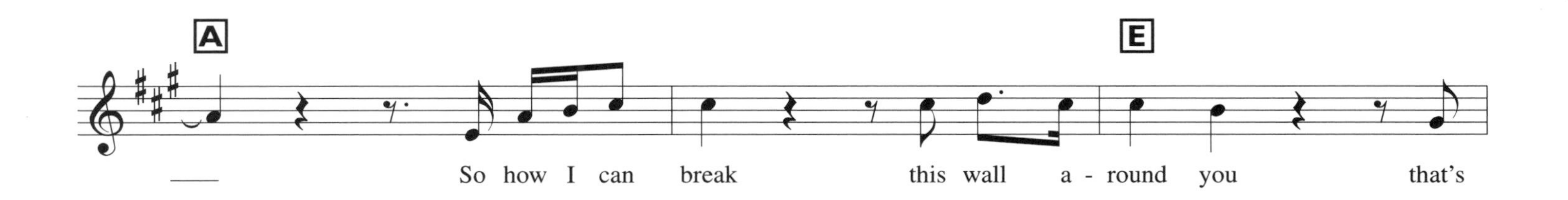
A
E
So how I can break this wall a - round you that's

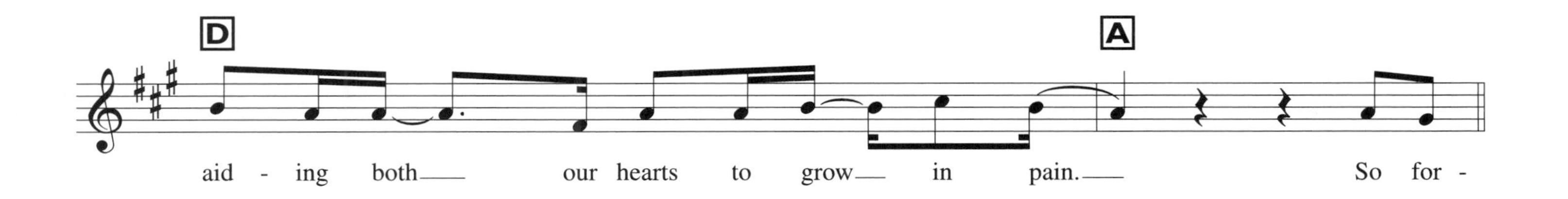
D
A
aid - ing both our hearts to grow in pain. So for -

D
E
C♯7
F♯m
D
E
- get your past and we can dream to - mor - row, save our hearts for care and lov - in'

F♯m
D
E
C♯7
F♯m
too. It's hard, I know, but oh, one thing's for sure, don't

D
E
A
N.C.
go and break this fra - gile heart. A hurt - ing

B
F♯
E
mind in need of e - mo - tion, I don't think it could en - dure an - oth - er pain.

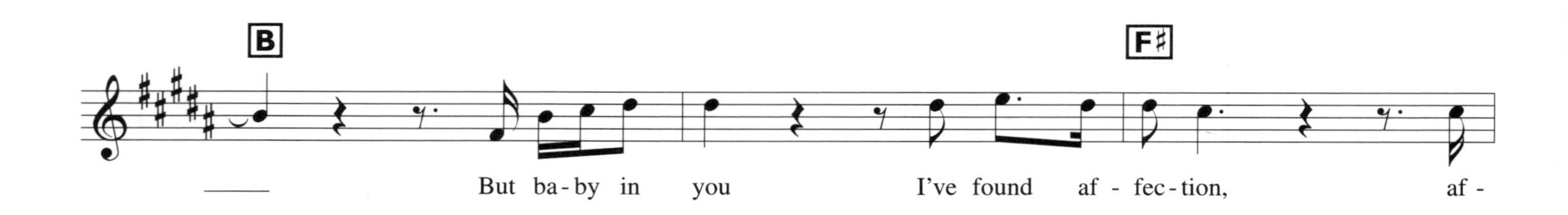
B
F♯
But ba-by in you I've found af - fec-tion, af -

E
B
- fec - tion I have nev - er felt be - fore. So don't

E
F♯
D♯7
G♯m
E
let your past des - troy what comes to - mor - row, don't go and break this fra - gile

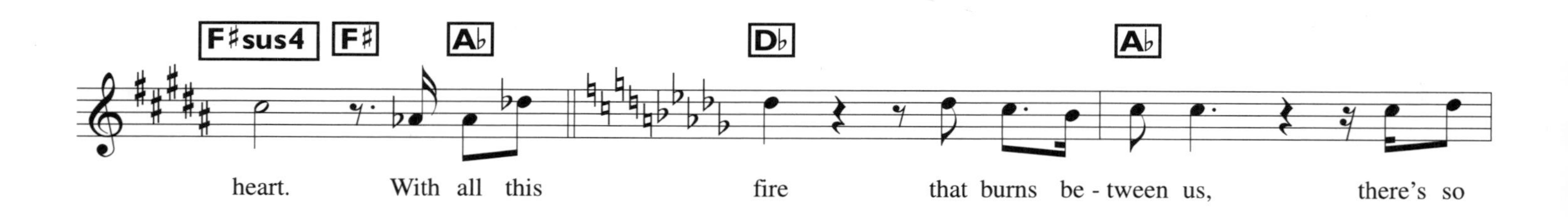
F♯sus4
F♯
A♭
D♭
A♭
heart. With all this fire that burns be - tween us, there's so

G♭
A♭
D♭
much to lose, yet so much more to gain. And if I could choose the world a -

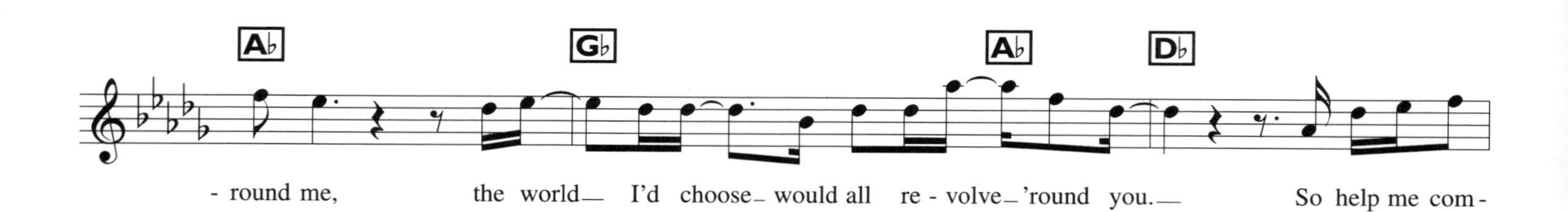
A♭
G♭
A♭
D♭
- round me, the world I'd choose would all re - volve 'round you. So help me com -

rall.
A♭
G♭
D♭/F
E♭m7
D♭
- plete the game in - side me and help to mend, to mend this fra-gile heart.